How to lose weight without dieting

Prentice Hall LIFE

If life is what you make it, then making it better starts here.

What we learn today can change our lives tomorrow. It can change our goals or change our minds; open up new opportunities or simply inspire us to make a difference. That's why we have created a new breed of books that do more to help you make more of your life.

Whether you want more confidence or less stress, a new skill or a different perspective, we've designed *Prentice Hall Life* books to help you to make a change for the better. Together with our authors, we share a commitment to bring you the brightest ideas and best ways to manage your life, work and wealth.

In these pages we hope you'll find the ideas you need for the life you want. Go on, help yourself.

It's what you make it

***

How to lose weight without dieting

Be the size you want to be for life

Jessica Robbins

Pearson Education Limited
Edinburgh Gate
Harlow
Essex CM20 2JE
England

First published 2007

Some names and location details have been changed to protect identities.

ISBN: 978-0-273-71340-1

Commissioning editor: Emma Shackleton
Project editor: Patricia Burgess
Text editor: Sarah Sutton
Copy editor: Ruth Baldwin
Index: Kathie Gill
Text and cover design: Annette Peppis
Production controller: Neil Wilmot

Printed and bound by Henry Ling, UK

The Publisher's policy is to use paper manufactured from sustainable forests.

CONTENTS

INTRODUCTION

Many people who struggle with their weight suffer a sense of isolation and low self-esteem. I know because I count myself among them. I struggled to overcome my issues with food and weight for 27 years. I hid behind fat as I grew up, choosing to miss out on adventures and life's experiences. I watched enviously as my sisters went out each evening looking slim and attractive, brought home boyfriends and told stories of what they'd been up to. Being overweight was my excuse for everything. I didn't go out because I had nothing to wear that didn't make me look fat. I believed I couldn't make friends because I was fat and that no one liked me because I was fat. I believed that no boy would ever fancy me or love me because I was fat. I was unhappy because I was fat – or so I thought at the time – and that was my excuse for doing ... nothing.

My weight increased year on year as I grew up, and I believed that only by starving myself or going on the latest fad diet would I lose weight. During short periods when I was 'thin', I thought all my problems had been solved, but starvation diets are not sustainable, so each time, after about one month, the weight gradually went back on.

One day, at the end of my latest starvation diet, as I stood in front of the mirror scrutinising my newly achieved size-10 body, I became aware of a voice inside my head telling me how fat my thighs were looking. The voice also told me that I was pathetic, I would always be fat, and that if I was no longer losing weight, then I must be putting it on. This was ludicrous and suddenly I knew it. Just a few weeks earlier I had been thrilled with my weight loss. For the first time in my life I realised that no matter what size I was, I was programmed to find myself ugly. It was a major turning point. I suddenly realised that my self-image was faulty, and no diet would change that.

As I listened more closely to this inner voice, I realised it sounded familiar. In a flash I was transported into my past, and heard the way my mother used to talk about herself. She was always dieting and would constantly criticise herself, saying she was 'fat *and* disgusting', as if one equated with the other. She would say, 'It doesn't matter what I do, I can't lose weight' or 'I only have to look at a cream cake and I put on weight.' I also recalled the words of my father, who used to tell me, 'You're just big-boned'. These and other 'helpful' comments were transformed into personal beliefs that I would hold for years to come.

At 10 years old and weighing 8½ stone (54 kg), I was confused that while nothing pleased my parents more than seeing me eat all my dinner, the children at school teased and bullied me every day of my life for being fat. (I now realise that they were teasing me because I was a victim of low self-esteem, not fat.) This was the point when I first became aware that it was food that made you fat. I have always been a logical soul, so when a neighbour introduced me to the idea of calorie counting, I lost no time in embarking on my first-ever starvation diet. At the age of 10 I was eating as few as 150 calories per day.

Our feelings make us fat

The truth is that our feelings can lead us to become overweight. Of course junk food, a high-fat diet, lack of exercise, poverty or genetics all play their part too. But the reality is that many of us use food to fulfil our emotional needs. I know I did, and at my lowest ebb, when I thought I would have to struggle with my weight forever, I even considered suicide. Only the thought of the paramedics looking critically at my fat dead body prevented me. It's shocking to think that vanity saved my life, but that was the case.

The issue of fat is a serious one. The obesity crisis is costing the taxpayer millions of pounds a year, but it also costs us in terms of lost living. It scares me to see the fast rise in the number of obese teenagers, along with the increase in stomach-stapling operations, and the lack of counselling back-up. We are led to believe that overweight people are lazy or stupid. After all, it's obvious, isn't it? You just do more exercise and eat less food and then you'll no longer be fat. If only it were that simple.

My weight gain, like many others', was a symptom of a much deeper problem. My complete lack of self-esteem and confidence (most of it learnt from my mum's behaviour towards herself); the fact that I hated my body because of the bullying; a lack of friends and extreme loneliness; the beliefs I held about myself and the world; the food habits I had learnt and the love/hate relationship with food that had developed as a result – all these factors contributed to my subconscious use of food as a means of comfort, control and pleasure.

Once my eyes were opened in my twenties, I set out on a journey of personal discovery, armed with some important questions:

- Why was I so successful in all other areas of my life, but had failed so miserably in this one?
- How could I gain back the personal power that I'd let slip away over the years?
- What did I need to change about what I was doing?
- What did I need to change about the way I was thinking?

- What beliefs did I need to change?
- How could I use the way my body worked to my advantage?
- How could I prevent others from going through what I had?
- Where did I want to end up?

This book is a result of the learning curves I went through to get to where I am today, as well as the work that I've done with my clients to help them achieve their dreams. Inevitably, I had to go down some blind alleys before I reached my current position, but I have consolidated everything you need to know so that you can do it more quickly and enjoyably than I did.

Taming the monster

The decision to write this book came after a conversation with a very close friend who had suffered with weight problems similar to mine. A couple of months previously she had run out of energy to control the 'monster', as she called her compulsion to eat, so it had taken over for a while. However, she now felt strong again and the monster was back under control. By this she meant that she was weighing and measuring every morsel of food she ate, was following a diet regime and watching the clock until the next mealtime. Her weekly food allowance was rigidly allocated, and her one day off a week was marked on the calendar. She was unhappy: the monster was ruling her life and, worst of all, she felt she had no choice in the matter.

I asked her whether she had ever considered the possibility of 'taming' the monster. I could see in her eyes that this is what she longed for. Had I already written the book, I would have handed her a copy there and then.

It was this conversation that made me realise I had to write the ultimate weight-loss book – the last one that anyone would ever have to read. In my greater dreams the book would end the obesity war and set people free of the cycle of dieting forever. Having tamed the monster, they would enjoy life to the full.

Are you really ready?

How to Lose Weight without Dieting is not a diet book. I am not going to prescribe a 14-day meal plan, give you weights and measures, advise on maximum grams of fat per day, or tell you not to eat chocolate if you haven't 'earned the points'. Instead, you will find information that will empower and help you to lose weight. You are going to learn new and easier ways of living, and strategies for satisfying your cravings in positive ways that don't involve food. Once these methods become new habits, you will never have to think about them consciously again.

Before we start, you have to be willing to consider that you are going to be *free*. Really and truly and honestly *free*.

Your mind can make you slim

Before you embark upon any change, whether small or life-changing, it's important to know what you want the outcome to be. What is it that you want to achieve by reading this book? Start to get a picture in your mind of what your ideal result would be. Feel in your body the changes you want to bring about and the excitement of being able to make a change that lasts for a lifetime.

At the heart of this book, and at the heart of all the changes in my life, are the principles of Neuro-Linguistic Programming (NLP) and self-hypnosis. NLP is a long phrase to describe a straight-forward concept. NLP uses the way that your mind works to reprogram your habits and behaviours. It enables you to adopt a more positive outlook, and to develop useful strategies to improve your life. Hypnotherapy uses deep, guided meditation techniques that affect change at the deepest level of consciousness. Together these techniques are a powerful and effective way to change the cycle of self-destructive behaviours associated with weight gain. NLP and hypnotherapy use the power of language to change your mind and therefore your self-perception. If you can change your self-perception, you will change your behaviour too.

All you need is a willingness to ask yourself questions and the curiosity to understand what makes you tick. I want you to discover the personal beliefs that are preventing you from having the body you desire, and I wish you the tenacity to persist until you get what you want.

The book outlines three core requirements that will enable you to reshape your habits, lose weight and tone your body:

1 Redefine your identity and the beliefs that will help you be who you want to be.
2 Find new, empowering ways of meeting your emotional needs so that you don't need to fill up with food.
3 Take responsibility. Learn to listen to your body and adopt the eating habits of healthy, happy people.

Each of these will be covered in the eight stages that follow.

Getting started on your path

Throughout this book you will find in-depth explanations, guidelines and exercises. They have been designed to help you progress on your personal journey as you read from cover to cover (though I would not like to stifle your individuality and prevent you from reading in whichever way pleases you most). There is also a summarising paragraph with the action plan at the end of each chapter. If you want to scan these sections first to get an overview, please do.

Being overweight or living in fear of putting on weight is like being in quicksand: the more you struggle to climb out, the deeper you sink. But it doesn't have to be that way. Learning the techniques of NLP and hypnotherapy changed every aspect of my life. They provided me with the new perspective that I needed to view my relationship with food in a different way. After years of hating myself and my body, I was able, within a surprisingly short time, to let go of my previous habits and step into an amazing new world where food is just food and I can appreciate myself for who I am. The exhausting and painful war between my body and my mind came to an end, and now, in this book, I share with you the secrets I learnt.

All you have to do is read this book, make the subtle and not-so-subtle changes suggested, and let them begin to take place *now*, all by themselves. You might find that everything you read makes sense to you, regardless of what you have been conditioned to believe. You are free to let your old beliefs and old decisions about food fall away, like leaves falling from a tree, making room for new and healthy leaves to grow in their place.

Taking action is empowering. It is also the simplest way for you to see instant progress and to develop belief in your ability to bring about lasting change. The most important thing to remember is that whatever happens along the way, you are improving your self-awareness and learning from your behaviour the reasons for the choices that you make. There is no 'failure' on the Jess Robbins' path; just the feedback the experience has given you so that you can make new choices and start again.

Good luck and let's get started!

JESSICA BEFORE AND AFTER NLP CHANGED HER LIFE.

STAGE 1
ANYTHING IS POSSIBLE

In my work I help many people to take back control of their life. I never cease to be amazed by what people can achieve once they develop self-belief and want something strongly enough. My experiences have led me to ask the question, 'Is anything possible?' and to choose to believe that 'YES! Absolutely ANYTHING is possible'.

It is not the universe we live in that determines our personal limits, but our own mind and imagination! By choosing to learn from situations in your life and stop focusing on emotions and injustices, you will grow and become more successful and happy. If you choose to see that all events have positive meaning, your life will become a constant stream of learning and gratitude.

Beliefs have power

What are your beliefs about yourself right now?

'I am big boned.'
'I'm weak-willed.'
'I have a slow metabolism.'
'We're all big in my family.'
'I eat when I'm bored.'
'I eat because I'm stressed.'
'I eat because I'm depressed.'
'I've tried, but I just can't lose weight.'

If you are currently overweight or have struggled with your weight throughout your life, you might have a number of beliefs as to why this is so. Your beliefs create your reality; meaning that whatever you believe will affect your actions, which in turn means that your beliefs will be gradually reinforced and will persist. For example, if you believe that losing weight is hard work, you will create that as your reality.

Our beliefs act like a filter through which we experience the world. We literally filter out all the evidence that contradicts our beliefs. If you have a belief that says, 'I can't lose weight', you will only pay attention to the times you weren't successful, or look for reasons to reinforce this belief.

One of the laws of physics is called the 'universal law of attraction', which states that 'like attracts like'. Hence, anger attracts more anger, hate attracts more hate, love attracts more love, wealth attracts more wealth, happiness attracts more happiness, and so on. Remembering that like attracts like, we should not be surprised that a belief that you can't lose weight will therefore attract ... more weight. However, you'll be glad to know that, whatever beliefs you currently hold, you certainly *can* lose weight.

There is always a way to prove that your old beliefs are false and to replace them with your own new, empowering beliefs. The exercises in this book will help you to see how you might have unknowingly attracted unwanted emotions and situations into your life and, more importantly, will help you to change, to ensure you attract exactly what you want from now on.

Choose your beliefs

Just because you haven't been able to lose weight in the past doesn't mean that it can't be done; it just means you haven't found the right way to achieve your goal yet. Sometimes our old beliefs are ridiculous, but we hold on to them out of habit. The belief 'I can't lose weight' is certainly not true. Anyone who was forcibly starved for a month would most definitely lose weight. Without food, our bodies lose weight, muscle breaks down and eventually we waste away. Biologically, this is a simple fact of life, isn't it? So the belief that 'I can't lose weight' is wrong thinking. Instead, rephrase the belief to become 'So far I haven't found a way to lose weight and stay slim'. This immediately allows the possibility that weight loss is achievable. I remember vividly how it felt to open my eyes to this possibility for the first time. I then began to see how I might achieve what I wanted. Losing weight and finding yourself go hand in hand, and it is an enlightening experience. I want to help you to discover how to break through the barriers that have been placed between you and your body and discover that your body is wonderful.

Take another look at the statements listed on page 15 and see how they make you feel. Do they empower you or hinder you? Now replace them with the following thoughts:

'I have great bone structure.'
'I can achieve anything I put my mind to.'
'I can speed up my metabolism.'
'We can all lose weight in my family.'
'I want something to do, not something to eat.'
'I need to relax, not eat.'
'I want to be filled with happiness, not filled with food.'
'I'm bored, not hungry.'
'I'm stressed, not hungry.'
'I'm depressed, not hungry.'
'I know I can lose weight.'

Do you feel more positive and more in control now?

A fantastic tip for feeling more positive is to act as if you already have the thing you want and to feel grateful for it. This confuses your mind because it can't find any evidence that you have what you want, so it will seek to create the evidence. This manifests itself in you subconsciously taking action to achieve it.

For example, if you want to be slim, be grateful for how slim you are now. Tell yourself: 'I am grateful for my slim body...' and you will begin to feel that you are slimmer than you thought you were. This will attract more thoughts and actions related to being slim, and you'll achieve your goal more quickly. (There is more about this on page 143.)

Take a look inside your mind

Imagine the whole of your mind as a dark, expansive space connected to the rest of the universe. Your *conscious mind* is like a torch, shining a light on a small patch of this space at any one time. What the torch shines on is what you're aware of right now. The rest is your *subconscious mind*. Part of its job is to run and monitor your life-support systems, such as your heart, your lungs and your digestion. It also controls your memory and your emotions, and deals with beliefs and values – your life's rules and priorities. Crucially, it also oversees your fears, hopes and dreams.

Now try to imagine your subconscious mind as so vast and unlimited that it has no boundaries. It is bigger and more expansive than the confines of your brain. How big can you imagine it to be? Only you can put limits on the true size of your mind. And remember – it is always larger and more powerful than you can possibly imagine. Your imagination is hampered by the fact that in the darkness, the torch of your conscious mind can see only as far as the torch has power to shine. As your eyes acclimatise to the dark, your conscious mind will be aware of more and more of what's going on in your subconscious mind.

The purpose of this book is to shine the torch of awareness deeper and deeper into your subconscious mind so that you are able to tap into the enormous scope of your full potential – to overcome your fears, and to realise your hopes and dreams.

Your mind and the tools of influence

As a peak performance coach and therapist, I use techniques and tools that can bring about changes in personal perspective at incredible speed. My work is grounded in the techniques of Neuro-Linguistic Programming (NLP) and hypnotherapy. With these methods you can create or alter your thoughts, feelings and behaviours to become the kind of person you want to be and have the life you want to lead. Changes in the way you think and feel, and therefore the way you behave, can be achieved within hours. Problems that you have lived with all your life will be reframed in your mind and disappear.

What is Neuro-Linguistic Programming?

NLP was first developed in the 1970s by Richard Bandler, a psychologist, and John Grinder, a linguistics expert. They studied the thinking and behaviour of successful people who were also great communicators in the area of personal transformation. Bandler and Grinder wanted to understand how these people achieved such incredible results, and their discoveries (known as 'behavioural modelling') led to the beginnings of NLP. It is a way of using positive thinking and visualisation to stop unhelpful ways of thinking and behaving, while choosing new and constructive thoughts and actions that will bring about positive change. The techniques aim to get results as quickly and efficiently as possible.

Neuro is to do with our thoughts, the nervous system and how information is processed via the brain.
Linguistic is to do with verbal and non-verbal language, and how we communicate with ourselves and others.
Programming is to do with the way we apply our thoughts and words, and how they combine to influence our actions and behaviour.

NLP also helps you take charge of your emotional state. Perhaps you know people who get angry or sad and seem to think that something outside them is 'making' them feel or act a certain way. NLP techniques can help to manage emotions and internal thought processes so that you can choose your frame of mind rather than reacting to the state of mind that you might have found yourself in. NLP is about taking responsibility and thus regaining control.

What is hypnosis?

Hypnosis is a natural 'trance' state that alters your state of awareness, and is one of the oldest phenomena known to man. It is found in various forms in virtually every culture throughout the world. In fact, it was used as a therapeutic technique over 4000 years ago in ancient Egypt as a way of eliciting healing. It is now widely accepted as a method by which we may access our subconscious mind.

Hypnosis is defined as a state of mind, enhanced by (although not exclusively) mental and physical relaxation, in which your subconscious is able to communicate with your conscious mind. It is used as a way of bypassing the conscious mind to communicate directly with the subconscious mind and to get to the heart of a deep-rooted problem or thinking habit. When you hold on to a memory or an experience that is painful, the conscious mind pushes it away and stores it in the subconscious memory. The trouble is that it is very hard to move beyond something you resist, since the very act of resisting becomes an ongoing experience. Hypnosis can be used to help find out what you are resisting, enable you to understand it, change your experience of it, and finally help you to 'let it go'. It is also a way of suggesting your preferred behaviours, thoughts and feelings directly to your subconscious mind, bringing about often immediate and effortless change.

By experiencing or understanding something, you can move through it, past it and release it from your life. You can then choose to move on to a newer, fresher experience that is more relevant to what you want in your life.

What is self-hypnosis?

Self-hypnosis is a kind of directed meditation that is induced by the person entering the trance. However, whereas in meditation the aim is to 'empty' the mind, in self-hypnosis the aim is to introduce new and positive ways of thinking and acting. For example, you might want to change negative thoughts about your body ('I look fat and horrid') for positive and appreciative ones ('My curves are sensuous and I am beautiful'). Self-hypnosis is very easy to practise, is perfectly safe, and is one of the most pleasurable and yet productive ways to relax and communicate with your subconscious mind.

Start listening to your body

If you are currently overweight, you might be using food to change the way you feel rather than to nourish your body. Or you might have habits that lead to weight gain, such as eating when you're not truly hungry, starving then gorging, or eating in response to emotional triggers rather than physical ones. You might not even recognise what true hunger is any more, or associate it with negative feelings, such as fear and panic.

Whatever the reasons for your tendency to overeat, it is never too late to reprogram your habits so that you feel more satisfied on a healthier diet, and start to lose weight. I will show you how to listen to the subtle signs from your body, understand what they mean and how your lifestyle affects them. I will give you techniques and affirmations that will help you to learn to love yourself. My aim is to encourage you to enjoy your body and to find new and positive ways to fulfil your emotional needs. No matter what your weight is right now, you have everything you need to help you take control and feel good about yourself and your life.

Your body knows which foods it needs to stay alive, and which will help it to heal, repair and grow. A healthy body wants nourishing foods and knows how to recognise the signals of true hunger. The problem is that we have learnt to override the body's healthy signals and have gradually replaced them with unhealthy cravings for sweet, salty and fattening foods that upset the body's metabolism. Nor do we really know when we are hungry, or when we are full. We are 'out of sync' with our feelings and our bodies – and widespread obesity is the result.

> Now is the time to start listening to your body.

The five-minute body check

Please start by doing the following 'body check' activity. It is so simple to do, and is an important technique for learning to listen to your body and to increase your personal awareness of what your body needs. Repeat it often, and as many times as you like. It is the ideal way to 'fill up with breath' instead of food. It is also a useful way of getting ready to do the activities in this book.

Sit in a chair and get comfortable. Close your eyes and breathe deeply. Then consider and focus on your body. Start at your head, then work down through each limb and each area of your body towards your toes. Consciously check that your muscles are releasing the tension they have been holding; notice the temperature and the comfort level of each part of your body. Monitor your body for signs of pain, pleasure, hunger, thirst, tiredness, etc. Continue to breathe deeply into your belly and enjoy how relaxed you can become.

Use this technique for five minutes at a time; every day if you can.

Start to take action

The point of this book is not just to help you understand the reasons you are overweight, but to help you to change...permanently. And that means doing things differently. Many of the poor eating habits and emotional behaviours you have learnt have been there since childhood. The only way to change these is to take action and do things differently.

The activities (indicated by ●) at the end of each chapter will help you to experience the changes you need to make in order to transform your life. I strongly recommend that you actually *do* all the activities. It is very easy to take things in at a superficial level and to say, 'I now understand what's wrong', but that won't help you unless you *do* something about it too. If you feel reluctant to do the activities, ask yourself, honestly: has *thinking* about your life challenges helped you lose weight so far? Has denying or resisting uncomfortable emotions helped you lose weight? If not, then give my way a try and keep an open mind. I will help you to experience what you need to experience, feel what you need to feel, and then move through those feelings and out the other side.

By contrast, some of the exercises in this book will ask you to sit quietly with yourself and, without any judgements or self-criticism, just *be*. If you are anything like I used to be, your first thought might be, 'I don't have the time right now. If I understand the concept, I don't need to do it, right?' Wrong! The point of the exercise is not to predict what will happen when you do it; it's to do it and experience it.

Some of the emotions that emerge when you do the activities may be painful. Don't stop just because you feel uncomfortable. If you don't persevere with an exercise at precisely the moment when you experience negative emotion, you will turn avoiding your feelings into a habit. Live with the habit for long enough and you get so used to it that you will lose contact with your feelings. The great thing about uncomfortable feelings is that when you acknowledge them instead of avoiding or going deep within them, they lose their power and disappear. For example, think of an occasion when you disregarded your nervousness about trying something new and did it anyway. Within moments your fear probably disappeared and was replaced with a sense of adventure and positive possibility.

Finally, take away the pressure to 'succeed'. If you put yourself under pressure to lose weight fast, you will end up back on a fad diet and back on the old weight-loss treadmill. You deserve better than that. Remind yourself that just as it took a few months to learn to walk properly, so too it takes time to adopt a new habit or behaviour. No one gave up on you as a child because you didn't learn to walk immediately or because you fell over a couple of hundred times along the way. You got there in the end, and so you will again. Go slowly, encourage yourself whenever you see improvement in your behaviour, and celebrate your positive results with energy and love. After all, we're talking about personal freedom here, not just weight loss. Freedom from weight-loss diets and the rule of food is worth waiting for, isn't it?

One step at a time

Most of what I say will make immediate sense to you, but some parts of the book will require more of a leap of faith, as they will challenge some of your most deep-rooted, lifelong beliefs. Please remember to label all such challenges as coming from 'an interesting perspective', rather than dismiss them because they don't fit in with your current beliefs. Remember that your current beliefs may have been formed a long time ago, and are contributing to your overweight experience, so perhaps it's now time to try out some fresh ones.

> Minds are like parachutes ... they work best when they're open!
>
> THOMAS DEWEY, LAWYER AND POLITICIAN

I have written this book to show you how to answer your own questions, and the more you read, the more you'll understand at a deeper level. The more you start to see the positive effects of what I'm saying, the more faith you'll have to keep making personal changes and make your own decisions. Let me show you new ideas and, if they make sense to you, adopt them as your own. I want to help and support you through this journey of self-discovery and change, and ask you to remember the words of Thomas Dewey above.

STAGE 1 ACTION PLAN

Taking the first step on any journey is challenging and empowering. You have done it, and your future starts now! The activities in this chapter will help you to expand your personal expectations and encourage you to break free of your past habits and behaviours. By learning how to retune the power of your mind, you will transform your self-belief and break free of unhelpful limitations. I also invite you to make a personal commitment to yourself, in the form of a declaration or contract, that will inspire and help you to stay focused as you continue on your journey.

Break free of your limitations

Beliefs create your experience. In any situation we seek evidence to prove that our existing beliefs are right – even if they cause us problems. Take some time to think about the beliefs you hold about yourself and your life. They may be connected to food, nutrition and losing weight or anything else. In order to loosen these beliefs, just answer the following questions for each of the main beliefs you found.

- *How true does your belief feel? Use the scale of 1–5, where 1 is absolutely true and 5 is absolutely false.*
- *Has it been a helpful or unhelpful (limiting) belief? Keep a note of the helpful beliefs.*
- *If it's been unhelpful, how do you prove this belief is true in your life?*
- *Can you find one or more instances in your life when it hasn't been true?*
- *What would be a more useful and empowering belief to have?*

For a worked example and more tips on how to use this activity and put it into practice, visit my website (www.jessicarobbins.co.uk).

Looking back to the future

Take time to do the following guided visualisation exercise; then answer the questions.

1 *Think about yourself as you are now, living your life as it is now. Ask yourself:*

- *What might you have missed out on in the past because you wouldn't change?*
- *What opportunities do you know you have missed?*
- *Whom have you hurt or punished because of the way you feel about yourself?*
- *How have you made yourself suffer?*

2 *Now imagine that you can look into the future, many years from now, on a life path where you chose not to change. You kept your belief that perhaps one more diet will set you free, and continued losing and gaining weight, finally giving up hope and convincing yourself you don't care any more. Ask yourself:*

- *What else have you missed out on over the years?*
- *How do you feel about yourself?*
- *How have you affected your friends and family?*
- *How do you feel about life and the future?*
- *What would you say to convince the younger you to take action and take this different approach?*

3 *Finally, imagine that you read this book and passionately engaged in changing your attitude and your life. You have* *reached your ideal weight and are now living the transformation. Ask yourself:*

- *How do you feel about yourself?*
- *How free do you feel?*
- *What else have you achieved through your new attitudes?*
- *How does it feel to be able to wear the clothes you love?*
- *What would you like to say to yourself in appreciation of your tenacity and self-respect?*
- *What opportunities have you benefited from?*
- *What would you like to say to yourself in appreciation of your tenacity and self-respect?*
- *What needed to change in your life to enable you to achieve and maintain your ideal weight?*

Did you notice how your mood and feelings changed as you moved through each step? Did you feel empowered by the sense of the possible during step 3? Remember – anything is possible if you choose to make it so. As a sign of your commitment to yourself, make the decision to change. Right now.

Your contract with yourself

You're about to embark on a journey of self-discovery that will result in you learning more about yourself than you ever thought possible. I invite you to make a promise and commitment to yourself here and now to give yourself the care and attention you deserve to help you bring about positive change in your life.

Signing a contract of agreement is a powerful symbol of commitment. Read the following aloud and think about what this contract means to you. Fill in the blanks and sign it, if you feel ready to make this promise to yourself.

You can even get a piece of paper and write today's date on it. Underneath, write 'This is the day I decided to change my life' and sign it. Pin it to the wall next to any photos you have of you at your ideal weight.

I, ______________________________

hereby promise to make it my intention:

To nurture my mind, body and soul for the rest of my incredible life.

To start listening to my body and respond compassionately and appropriately.

To do what I need to do in order to fall in love with myself and my body.

To move my body for pure enjoyment and because it deserves to feel wonderful.

To seek out different activities until I find something my body enjoys doing.

To embark upon the most amazing, intimate and loving relationship I will ever have – with myself – recognising and cherishing my body for the loyal companion it is.

To forgive myself and others for any hateful feelings I or others have shown towards it.

To stop punishing and hurting myself, and to show my body the respect it deserves. To give it my time and attention.

To allow my body to sleep when it's tired, eat when it's hungry, drink when it's thirsty, remove it from harm's way and take action when it's energetic.

To be more positive about my life as I know a positive emotional state improves my immune system and floods my body with feel-good hormones, allowing me to be happy and handle situations more effectively.

To give my time and attention to those who love, support and encourage me in order to send a strong message to myself that I am worth loving.

To take the time to ensure my needs are met, and have the courage to follow my dreams.

To give time to setting my goals and take quiet time each day to focus my mind on the lessons I have learnt and what I want tomorrow to bring.

To keep going and removing old beliefs until I get what I want and enjoy every step of my journey.

To wake up each day as if I did it on purpose!

Signed ______________________________

Date ______________________________

STAGE 2
FACING UP TO FOOD AND FEELINGS

One of the most dangerous characteristics of being overweight is holding a distorted view of your own reality. While someone who is anorexic has the distorted view that they are too fat, a compulsive overeater from a family where everyone is overweight might hold the distorted view that their size is healthy and normal; similarly, someone who has bought a pair of jeans a size smaller than is comfortable might go on a crash diet to fit into them when they just needed to 'wise up' and buy a larger size. If you are always dieting and still feel you need to lose weight, it is time to get to know yourself and your habits, and to learn to understand your thoughts and your body. Other people might already know more about you than you know yourself since their perspective will differ from yours.

Changing your perspective

Getting to know yourself through other people's eyes can help you to get to know yourself better. How many times have you talked to a friend about a problem only to find she sees things in a totally different and more positive light than you? And when you've changed to her perspective, don't things start to look a bit better? This approach can apply to understanding more about your body image too. Choosing to listen to our nearest and dearest, and learning that we are holding a distorted view of ourselves can give us a benchmark to work from.

Think of those you can trust to answer your questions honestly, and get ready to ask them for some feedback. If people are constantly telling you that you really don't need to lose weight, perhaps you're not as big as you think you are.

On the other hand, they might be very worried about your health or how sad you are about your size and desperately want to help you. By asking direct questions you invite their interest and give them permission to offer you support. The best person to ask for a completely honest answer is your GP. He or she will answer your questions objectively and with your health in mind rather than whether you fit into your new jeans. How you interpret the information you are given is up to you. You can find a way to feel good or bad about it, or just see it as useful information that will help you move forward.

Avoid a 'no win' situation

Consider carefully before asking your partner for their opinion. Can he or she speak openly and honestly with you about this issue without you becoming offended? Can you truly accept their reply? If you believe that your current size or shape makes you unlovable, it might make it impossible for them to give you the 'right' answer without upsetting you.

The definition of a problem is the difference between how you want things to be and how they are now. Fitting into a size 16 isn't a problem if you used to be a size 18, but it might be a problem if you were a size 14 until recently. Even then, it becomes a problem only if you are unhappy about being a size 16 and feel you can do nothing about reducing your weight.

In order to solve any problem, we need to understand our starting point, and how we got to it. I invite you to take a *realistic* view of what's currently going on in your body and mind so that you can see what needs to change. The reason I stress 'realistic' is that we must not see things as worse than they really are. Although it might feel as if your world is ending because the scales aren't going in the right direction, you need to get things into perspective and to see them as they really are. Facing up to the truth just as it is, and without judgement, can help motivate you to make some sensible changes.

The choice of change

I almost choked when my GP told me I was clinically obese 10 years ago. Until that point, my biggest concern about my weight had been whether or not I could wear a bikini. It had never occurred to me that my weight was affecting my health. Suddenly, being overweight was life threatening and had become something I had no choice but to change.

Every problem has a root cause. This chapter looks further at the personal triggers and beliefs that might cause you to overeat so that you can identify more clearly what you want to change. The cause usually lies in one of the following:

- Your emotions
- Your habits
- Your associations

And sometimes the cause can involve all three.

The hierarchy of human needs

We all have basic needs, each of which must be met in turn in order to survive. Based on a hierarchy of needs first identified by a psychologist called Abraham Maslow in 1945, they may be grouped as follows:

1 We need to feel alive – so we need food, water, sleep, movement, excitement and warmth.
2 We need to feel safe – so we try to stay away from pain or harm.
3 We need to feel we belong – so we search for connection and love from others.
4 We need to feel significant – so we seek attention and recognition to feel that we matter.

Until these basic-level needs are met, we are unable to fulfil our higher-level needs:

5 We need to feel fulfilled – we have a sense of purpose and want to realise our full potential.
6 We have spiritual needs – the need for a higher form of love. We feel connected to the rest of the universe and make our life about more than just ourself.

When we are able to meet all these needs, we experience emotional or physical pleasure. When we are not meeting them, we feel physical or emotional pain.

6 We have spiritual needs.
5 We need to feel fulfilled.
4 We need to feel significant.
3 We need to feel we belong.
2 We need to feel safe.
1 We need to feel alive.

How behaviour meets our emotional needs

We are each driven by a compulsion to move away from pain and towards pleasure, whether physical or emotional. For example, when we are hungry we want to move away from the pain of the hunger towards the pleasure of a satisfied stomach; and when we are distressed we want to move away from that pain towards the pleasure of feeling comforted. (See 'Problematic associations' on page 42.) The hunger instinct is fascinating, especially for those who have a battle with their weight, because it is so closely related to the basic instinct for human survival (to eat), and is also associated with feeling loved, secure and nurtured as well (to be comforted).

Take a look at the hierarchy triangle opposite. Food can potentially fulfil all of the first four levels of need. As well as making us physically full and therefore healthy, the receiving of food makes us feel safe, and a rush of blood to the stomach makes us feel alive, provides a sense of belonging and gives us the knowledge that we matter. Many of our emotional associations with food develop during childhood. Most of us discover from birth that if we are distressed, we are fed. As adults, we remember this and might decide to treat ourselves with food because we are 'good' or in need of comfort, and then punish ourselves for being 'bad' and overeating. Likewise, food becomes associated not only with the pain of physical hunger, but also with the pain of emotional hunger. Is it any wonder that many people turn to food for comfort in vulnerable moments of grief, stress, fear or insecurity?

How your emotional needs trigger weight gain

Most of us in developed countries are able to meet our physiological needs for food, shelter and warmth. However, our need to feel safe and secure can be more difficult to achieve and sustain. Anything that makes us scared or nervous is interpreted by the body as a threat, so developing a freedom from fear is crucial to fulfil this need. You face stresses and anxieties every day – a boss who gives you a hard time, a high-pressure job, the threat of redundancy, your partner leaving you, unfamiliar places, meeting new people, and so on – all these 'fears' threaten your sense of security on a daily basis. Maslow's theory says that we can't meet our higher-level

Your fairy godmother – nurturing

A powerful way of filling up without food is to retrain your internal dialogue so that you always speak to yourself warmly and positively. By imagining that you have a nurturing, loving and supportive fairy godmother who thinks you're wonderful, you can guarantee that you will be encouraged in certain behaviours and discouraged in others.

Your fairy godmother is your surrogate parent, and she will re-parent the parts of you that are crying out for clear guidance. She is there whenever you need her, ready to say something encouraging, inspiring, motivational and helpful. As you become more aware of your daily thoughts, start to block the unhelpful ones and instantly replace them with your fairy godmother's uplifting comments. After a while, as with any new habit, the new, positive thoughts will

needs until we meet the ones below them. If our higher-level needs remain unfulfilled (i.e. we don't get the love we want or don't feel our life has significance), we are more likely to try to find fulfilment *through* those lower-level needs. Like children, we will seek instant gratification and comfort, or might throw a 'tantrum' through the frustration of not getting what we want. Just as a child will suck his thumb or look for a comforter, all too often the quickest and easiest adult route takes the form of food, alcohol, cigarettes or drugs.

How food fills the needs gap

Our health and physiological needs are the first-tier priority. Food equals personal survival at this level. Security is the

begin to occur naturally and your behaviour will improve by itself. This might sound too good to be true, but it really works. You get to be treated the way you always wanted to be treated and, as a result, be the person you always wanted to be. I am the living proof that this works – as are many of my clients!

When I started swimming regularly it took me a few months to realise that I'd been getting up early and going to bed on time without fail in order to achieve my target, and yet my fairy godmother's voice had neglected to mention that it was a positive behaviour. When I 'switched on' her voice it felt really great to give myself a much-deserved 'well done' and boost to my ego. After all, given that I was 29 years old, it was unreasonable to expect my own parents to get up at 5 a.m. to come and watch me swim!

second-tier priority. In my view, the more scared you are of things in your life, the less fulfilled you might feel and the more likely you are to turn to food as a source of comfort.

At the third level we have a strong need for social connection with other human beings, but if we're too shy or tired to connect with others, we connect with ourselves instead, and eat alone, or join others in the safest activity we know of, which is eating and drinking. The fourth-level priority is the need to feel respected and know that we matter. If our parents praised us for 'eating up' as a child, this easy route to a feeling of accomplishment can make its way into our adulthood too.

However, we can never feel fully satisfied unless we meet our higher-level needs too. We have an innate need for fulfilment: to be 'filled full'. If we neglect our desire for fulfilment or spiritual connection, we will constantly revert back to the needs at the bottom of the triangle in an attempt to feel more satisfied.

Of course, we will never feel satisfied if we eat or drink more than we physically need. When we overeat we're looking for the kind of nourishment from food that just isn't there. It is often both nutritionally and emotionally lacking.

How a repetitive behaviour creates a habit

Once we have found a behaviour that helps us fulfil one or more of our needs, we will repeat it because it satisfies or gives us comfort. The repetition of this behaviour causes it to become ingrained into the subconscious mind and it gradually becomes a habit. The brain makes no distinction between a 'good' habit and a 'bad' habit; both types are subconscious and automatic.

The brain finds habits incredibly useful because it means we don't have to think consciously about everything we need to do, and can therefore relax and do several things at the same time. Eating habits are no exception: whatever strategy stops you from starving will be considered functional by your subconscious mind, and your body will become trained to follow it repeatedly. The problems begin when your eating habits are triggered to meet your need for security, recognition, comfort or social belonging too. We look at habits in more depth as part of Stage 5.

How we associate food with behaviour

One of the ways the memory works is by making associations between cause (actions) and effect (emotions). During our life we have many experiences, and each of these is an action that will trigger an emotional outcome. Some we label as painful and others as pleasurable, depending on how they caused us to feel and the effect of the outcome.

For example, many people are terrified of public speaking: the very thought of it triggers feelings of humiliation or suffering. These people strongly associate the action (public speaking) with a negative emotion (fear/humiliation). If ever they encounter a similar situation, they are compelled to move away from it (from pain) towards anything else (more pleasurable).

For other people, public speaking is associated with great pleasure, since they receive accolades and, as a result, feel good about themselves. Their instinct will be to repeat this behaviour again because they associate it with a feeling of pleasure.

The point about developing associations is that you can use them to empower yourself with new and beneficial habits. If you want to break an old habit, one technique involves purposely and consciously associating huge amounts of pain with it so that you'll never want to do it again. (For example, you might have been in the habit of eating prawns until one day you got food poisoning from them.) Alternatively, you can choose to associate huge amounts of pleasure with the behaviour you *do* want. (For example, taking pleasure in knowing that you can soak in the bath for 30 minutes instead of having a snack when you're bored.)

As human beings, we are programmed to find instant change a bit frightening; we prefer change to occur at a pace that gives us time to adapt. However, there are many changes that are instant and very enjoyable, such as finding love or winning the lottery. This shows that you can change your behaviour instantly if the change is associated with huge amounts of pleasure and reward. If it's not, take things slowly and give yourself time to adapt to new behaviours.

Problematic associations

It's all too easy for problem associations with food/eating to be created, and you can end up seesawing between pain and pleasure. To help you envisage how this works, think of a set of old-fashioned weighing scales. On one side is PLEASURE and on the other side is PAIN. We ideally want the balance on both sides to be equal and COMFORTABLE, or tipped in favour of pleasure.

When we do something that is pleasurable and has no negative consequences, this adds to the pleasure side (for example, enjoying a movie or making love with your partner). If, over time, the intensity of the pleasure effect wears off, the scales will tip back to comfortable on the pain–pleasure scale.

When you overeat, the effects are temporary in the short term on the pleasure scale, but permanent and painful in the long term on the pain scale. The balance shifts only temporarily in favour of pleasure before swinging back to pain when your stomach is empty. If this short-term pleasure causes a permanent increase in your body weight, the pain side of the scale will need to be increased accordingly. You know you need to put the balance back to comfort or pleasure again, so what do you do?

Your brain will tell you to do whatever brings you pleasure. If, for example, choosing to go to a party means too much pain in the short term (due to fear about what to wear, anxiety about meeting people, the inconvenience of getting home), in spite of potential pleasure in the long term (meeting new friends, having more invitations), the short-term pleasure of choosing more food will be more appealing in comparison. The scales try to swing again towards pleasure, but find it difficult because you have added further permanent weight to the pain side of the scale.

Eventually, the scales become so heavily weighed down on the pain side that you opt to go on a weight-loss diet – until the scales are balanced back at comfortable. It is therefore important to adjust your perception of what a comfortable body weight is for you, as well as being aware of your ideal body weight. It is also vital to be alert to the associations you have with activities and whether they cause pain and pleasure.

While you're in the state of *fat*, you're comfortable. You are *eating* what you want, which means you experience *pleasure* when you eat and comfort at other times. You gradually put on weight, until one day you experience *clothes not fitting* and feel huge pain. Your instinct compels you to move away from this experience to find pleasure immediately.

Let's say you decide to eat, since *eating* brings immediate pleasure and you enter a cycle of *eating* and feeling bad. After a while of more and more *clothes not fitting*, and *eating* as a response, you are now obese. This is huge pain, so your conscious mind may realise that *eating* leads to huge pain. To get out of the pain of being obese, you go on a diet because *dieting* and even *hunger* are less painful than being obese, and being *slim* will be pleasurable. You diet until you are at a weight that you call *fat* again and begin to feel comfortable. You want to move forward and be *slim*, but this means more *dieting* and *hunger* that are more painful than where you are. Since you are comfortable, your instincts tell you not to move into states that are painful, so you sabotage your diet with *eating*, to redress the pain–pleasure balance, or give up entirely, remaining at your comfortable level of *fat*.

Does this sound like the pattern you've experienced over the years? Dieting, gaining weight, dieting, gaining weight? Do you know which food associations you need to change in order to choose to get to and stay at *slim*?

The reality is that:

What you want most is happening right now.

This means that you are currently experiencing the most pleasurable state you believe you can achieve without exposing yourself to more pain than you can handle. Once your desire to lose weight becomes greater than your desire to keep the benefits you get from being 'feel good' fat, you will indeed lose weight.

If you choose not to change, it's because you're associating something painful with the process of change or the outcome of the change. If you don't change your associations, you will have to wait until you are really miserable, when the pain becomes so great (for reasons of health or vanity) that the pleasure–pain balance finally tips in favour of choosing to take action to lose weight and get healthy.

In order to help ourselves move into pleasurable states, we have to make sure that the behaviours we want are associated with huge amounts of pleasure, and the behaviours we don't want are associated with huge amounts of pain. Luckily, with the assistance of NLP, we have some conscious control over the associations we make in our mind, and the exercises that are used throughout the book will help you to achieve this.

Emotional associations with food

We all have a relationship with food. When we were babies, most of us cried when our tummy was empty and mummy would have picked us up, cuddled us and put something nice in our mouth – and, lo and behold, the pain went away. For most of us, food has on some level become associated with comfort and the cuddles and closeness of others. This relationship between food and emotions is reinforced throughout our life, with many social occasions being linked to food – the more intense the feelings, the more extravagant the meal; treats and comfort are associated with sweet treat such as chocolate; we celebrate by eating out or drinking alcohol; and then there are the times when 'takeaway' food saves us time and makes our lives easier and more fun.

Associations with hunger

Hunger has the power to trigger the pain of associated emotions with the pangs of hunger. In my own case, I suffered feelings of panic, a life-and-death fear so bad that I couldn't go to other people's houses unless I knew I would be able to control what I ate. 'What if there is no food, or I have to ask for it?' I would wonder. 'They'll think I'm greedy.' (See also page 6.)

I would pre-emptively overeat – all the time – so as not to feel that feeling. Similarly, any feeling of panic, fear or stress would trigger the same associations and convince me I was hungry, so that was a link I needed to break. The equation went like this:

Hunger = panic = fear = eat something

You too have many thoughts and feelings connected to food. There will be voices in your head that you'll discover are not yours, but whose advice you follow blindly without realizing it. I will teach you how to change this voice in Stage 6.

Recognising your trigger foods

Your emotions are easily associated with specific foods, and this knowledge is wired into your subconscious mind. For example, you might associate the words 'Sunday roast' with pleasurable memories of eating and bonding with your family, and the feelings of warmth that triggers. As a result, eating a Sunday roast will transport you back into that state of memory and will trigger the same pleasurable feelings you get from family bonding. In a similar way, negative associations with food can also become wired into your subconscious mind. If your family used to row and fall out at mealtimes, that same Sunday roast may be something you choose to avoid because it triggers pain and feelings of sadness or anxiety.

Going to extremes

Those who overeat have learnt that eating more than they need results in consequences that they associate with pleasure. In childhood these positive associations would have included rewards, such as praise, attention, love and so on, associated with 'eating up', being 'good' and 'eating nicely'. They might also have been motivated by a desire not to experience painful states, such as punishment, reprimand, parental anger, forced feeding, lack of attention or withdrawal of love, if they neglected to eat all the food on their plate.

While for overeaters food may equal pleasure, for another group of dieters, food equals pain. As children, we began to associate food with attention from the time we were born. All children crave attention, whatever form it takes. Some children work out that when they refuse to eat, Mum and Dad give them loads more attention. It might be negative attention, but it is attention all the same. They then realise that they can control the level of attention received depending on what and how they eat. These children feel powerful when they abstain from food, and an association is created that may be used later on in life whenever they feel less powerful than they'd like to feel. They are not sure why abstaining makes them feel more powerful, particularly if the parents have long since stopped taking an interest, but the old association is maintained. It is possible that those with a tendency to extreme dieting or anorexia have therefore learnt to associate the feeling of starvation with control, and control with pleasure.

Powerful associations

The aim throughout this book is to build your self-awareness. When you understand the associations and habits that are embedded in your subconscious mind, you will understand which of your outdated habits, associations or emotions are currently compelling you to overeat. Once you've recognised these causes, you can learn to replace them with powerful and pleasurable associations that trigger the behaviours you would like to adopt. I will show you techniques during Stage 2 that you will use literally to reprogram your mind with the thoughts, habits and associations you need in order to have the body you deserve.

Changing your state of mind

Our behaviour is caused by the emotional state we're in, which is governed by three elements:

Focus – what we think about or visualise.
Physiology – what's going on inside and outside our body that is reflected, for example, in our posture, or feelings of fatigue.
Language – what we say to ourself.

It is usually easier to change the trigger (the state we're in) that causes our behaviour than it is to change the behaviour itself. For example, it is easier to resist *buying* the supersized bar of chocolate (since we're only in that state for a moment) than it is to resist *eating* it once it is in the cupboard at home.

Changing one, two or all three of the elements that affect our emotional state (focus, physiology or language) and influence our choices will result in a different behavioural response.

When you start a weight-loss diet, you change your point of **focus**. You become more consciously aware of food, measuring it and counting calories, planning your next meal, and trying to distract yourself until you can eat again.You imagine how nice it will be when the diet has finished.Perhaps you change your focus so that you visualise the effect on your thighs if you eat a chocolate bar, and this puts you off. While your focus is on losing weight, this will change your behaviour. (However, once the diet is over, if your point of focus returns to where it was before, perhaps to finding comfort rather than staying slim, your old behaviours will return.)

What you eat also changes your **physiology**. When you change the foods you are putting into your body, you change your body chemistry and your internal physiology too. For example, you can change your behaviour triggers by choosing to eat more healthily. Complex carbohydrates (such as pasta, rice and cereals), for example, will slow your digestion, giving you a steady flow of energy, whereas eating sweets will make you feel very energetic for a short time and then trigger the craving for food again. Eating the healthy way will satisfy the hormones in your body that trigger the feelings of hunger.

You could choose to begin an exercise program in order to lose weight. Your muscles will start to build in strength and endurance, and the hormone levels in your body will change. You might feel stronger, more energetic, walk taller and hold yourself differently, so your behaviours change outwardly as well as inwardly. Regular exercise is a great way to lose weight, but unless it's a permanent habit change, the weight will go back on.

Of the three elements that make up our emotional state, the most powerful is **language**. What you say to yourself, either inside your head or out loud, can completely control you. We often call the negative voice 'the gremlin'. Without changing the way you speak to yourself, you will find it impossible to change your behaviour long term. (There's more about how to achieve this in Stage 6.)

Changing each of these elements as necessary will produce resourceful and positive states, and will enable you to develop just the behaviour you want, and ditch the behaviour you don't, giving you long-term success. You also need to develop the confidence to know that you can change your response should you accidentally revert to negative behaviour. The knowledge that you have conscious control over your thoughts, feelings and habits will give you the confidence to know that you are therefore also in control of your life. As with all conscious activities, once you have practised these skills, they themselves will become very helpful habits for you.

The power of belief

We all have our own unique view of who we are and how the world we live in works. The way we view the world is dependent on the large number of beliefs that we have collected through learning experiences as we've grown up. A belief is something we feel we know with 100 per cent certainty. A belief prevents us from having constantly to question the world around us. We need our beliefs in order to feel certain about the world we live in, and they give us a sense of predictability that makes us feel safe. They shape our life and our world, and determine our behaviours. Imagine you didn't have the ability to form beliefs. You would never know anything for sure and have to ask yourself the same questions every day. 'How do I know I'm alive? How do I know I'm a woman/man? Is that food safe to eat? Do I like coffee?' You'd have to go through the same process daily, and you'd have great difficulty making it out of the house in the morning to get to work!

We all have a level of scepticism that defines how much proof we need about something or how many times we have to test the validity of it before we believe it. Some of us believe everything we hear, some of us believe everything we see, and some of us believe only if we see it or experience it for ourselves. Others need to hear information from particular sources that are already deemed reliable. Once we have formed beliefs to make sense of our world, our brain will try to defend them so that we are not contradicted. It will look for information that backs up our current beliefs and will also ensure that they are reinforced by our life's events and our own behaviour. This causes what's known as the self-fulfilling prophecy, and in weight loss it can lead to many problems. In short, you create your experience based on the beliefs that you hold. If you don't like your experiences, it is advisable to stop perpetuating them by removing some of the beliefs you have about the world.

Limiting beliefs

Let's consider that your current life experience, whether positive or negative, is the result of all the beliefs you hold about yourself and the world. Most of the time we are not aware that we are operating under these belief systems, and often they are not beliefs we chose to adopt. Many beliefs will have been chosen for you when you were a child, or were created by you as a child, with a child's limited understanding of the world. As a child, you absorbed many beliefs from those around you, since it's much more efficient to do this than reinvent the wheel. These are called indoctrinated beliefs, and we are biologically programmed to adopt them for our own protection, as it would lower our risk of survival if, for example, our parents told us something was dangerous, but we daily chose to test it for ourselves. Your beliefs affect the way you think, feel and behave, and they are incredibly powerful. Once a belief is in your subconscious mind, it doesn't just 'fall out' accidentally.

The good news is that we can consciously influence which beliefs we hold. Very often the beliefs that are causing us the most problems in our life are the ones we are not consciously aware of, or those where we can't remember the situation that created them. These beliefs are problems because they feel so absolute and unquestionable. By realising their origin we are able to see just how irrational we were at the time, and, as a consequence, the belief is loosened and we are free to create a more useful one.

To start looking at the beliefs you hold currently about yourself and the world you need to be willing to do some 'housekeeping' so that your beliefs are working for you rather than hindering you. It's an easy process and has fantastic results. To change a belief, we might need to see proof that it is false, or realise that it couldn't be or doesn't have to be true.

You hear people's negative beliefs all the time, as they use them in almost every conversation. Anything someone thinks they know for sure is a belief. For example: 'I never win anything'; 'My memory is terrible'; 'I'm always late'; 'I don't have enough time'; 'My mother-in-law hates me'; 'My boss has it in for me'; 'I don't have enough money'.

These are limiting beliefs that are particularly damaging to us because they limit our options or abilities in some way. They act like a door inside our mind, which remains closed to possibility. If I tell you to move a rock, but also tell you that you are very weak and the rock is immovable, how much effort would you put into moving it? Would you even bother to try? Your brain behaves in the same way. If I tell myself that I can't lose weight, instead of saying, 'I don't seem to have mastered losing weight *yet*', I am closing the door inside my brain that looks to grow and develop my ability to transform my health. We are all guilty of talking in a way that limits our choices.

Whether you say you can or say you can't, you're right.

HENRY FORD III, INDUSTRIALIST

To deal with all the information that bombards your senses every day, your brain chooses to filter the information for you. If you had to pay attention to all of it, you'd be constantly overwhelmed. One of the filtering systems your mind uses is **deletion**. This cuts down on the *amount* of data to process. If data comes in that contradicts one of your beliefs, it will most likely be deleted. For example, look around the room and count how many red things you see. Then, without looking, recall how many blue things you saw. Your mind wasn't looking for blue, so it disregards information about blue things.

Another type of filter is **distortion**. This occurs when received information is altered to fit in with an existing belief or expectation. For example, if you've ever counted calories, you might distort the memory of how much you ate so that you don't have to count the true number of calories.

An example of filtering

Let's say I go on a diet and it doesn't work as I'd hoped. I feel disappointed and fed up. Feeling disappointed and fed up makes me blame the fact that I'm fat for my failure. I still want to lose weight. I try again and again. I still don't get the result I want. In an attempt to make myself feel better, I blame the world or my body and generalise my experience. I conclude that I definitely can't lose weight. I continue to try, but my brain is deleting the information that tells me I am losing weight, leaving in the information that says my thighs are fat, or my tummy is still wobbly, listening for the negative comments people make, and deleting or dismissing the compliments. My mind distorts the view of myself in the mirror, and in the end I feel so bad about what I'm doing that I give up. After all, if I can't lose weight, it's pointless trying, isn't it?

The final way of filtering information is via **generalisation**. If you try to lose weight once and it doesn't work, then you try again and it still doesn't work, you might generalise your experience by saying, 'I can't lose weight'. Your mind will then try to delete, distort and generalise your experiences to ensure that this remains true.

The power of positive language

The key to breaking through limiting beliefs is to realise that anything is possible, and just because you haven't achieved something yet, it doesn't mean you won't. You must phrase anything you say about your limitations in the form: 'I haven't been able to do that *yet*' or 'I haven't found a way to be this *yet*'. This keeps the part of your mind that looks for answers to problems well and truly on the case. Remember that *you* are in charge and *you* can change it if you want (see Stage 3). If you haven't found a way yet, it could be just around the corner. After all, remember the adage that says if you do what you've always done, you'll get what you've always got. This means that it's time for something new. Time to dust off your wonderful brain and get using it. Ask it challenging questions (see Stage 3), allow yourself to experience emotion and release it if necessary. Whatever the new approach, just find one and use it. You can have fun exploring your mind and enjoy breaking through what stops you.

Have you ever noticed how full of energy and optimism a young child tends to be? Life is full of possibilities and excitement when you are young. At one point, either before or after your birth, you were a completely unlimited being. The only limitation to you was the scope of your imagination.

One by one, layers of limitation were added to your experience of the world and your options decreased. However, you are now free to play with the idea that you are still unlimited, and if you choose to, you could let those imposed limitations fall away.

An exercise in power

Try writing a list of the limiting thoughts or beliefs you have. For each one, just imagine who you would be and what life would be like without that thought or belief. It's a powerful exercise!

If you chose to believe something more positive instead, how would life be different?

For example, how would life be if you believed you were as beautiful as your favourite Hollywood actress? How would you think, feel and act differently, and what would the long-term effects be? How would people respond differently to your behaviour?

Since we all chose our beliefs at some point in our lives (see page 52), couldn't you now choose to have a totally new set of beliefs that gives you unlimited choice and advantages in behaviour?

Sometimes it takes a bit of rewiring to change beliefs, so look at page 151, where I show you how to break them down and create the new, empowering beliefs you want.

STAGE 2 ACTION PLAN

The vital connection between food and feelings is at the very heart of what this book is about, and it is also at the very heart of who you are. The Stage 2 activities are fundamental to the whole 'weight-loss without dieting' process. You are about to discover new ways to fulfil your needs without resorting to using food for comfort. You will develop a creative way to change your self-talk by using conscious word association; and in order to find out what triggers your unwanted habits and behaviours, you will be encouraged to track your behaviour and see what motivates you to overeat or deprive yourself of food. Use these activities as often as you need them.

Fulfil your needs

1 *Using the following headings, write down all the ways in which you are currently meeting your needs.*

- *Love and/or connection*
- *Certainty and security*
- *Ego and significance*
- *Self-actualisation*

2 *Using the same headings as in the previous step, come up with at least two new ways for meeting each need that are not food-related. To help you, do the following:*

- *Think about ways that you fill your own needs from within yourself rather than from anything external. This will help you avoid dependency on someone or something to meet your emotional needs.*
- *Focus on thoughts that give you certainty or significance by concentrating on what's amazing about yourself, or the things you've achieved in your life. (Trust me, you are incred-*

ible!) By focusing on a thought that gives you a sense of fulfilment, you are fulfilled, so find something that when you think about it fills you up.

- *The best feeling of all is that of unconditional love. You can feel as much of this as you like by feeling it for someone else. Try this: think of someone you love or have loved unconditionally, or someone you know who you think is amazing.*
- *Now just focus your mind on that person and feel how much love you have for them. Let it build and build and build. Breathe it in and keep appreciating how brilliant and perfect they are. Does that feel good?*

Well, that's the secret. By giving unconditional love to someone else, you get to feel as much of it as you like. So by giving, you are always receiving. If you want to feel love, give love!

3 What does food do for you?

Pick a behaviour that you dislike, or your issue with food in general, or a habit or a situation you'd like to understand better or want to change. Then ask yourself, 'What does it do for me?' (For example, 'What does eating chocolate do for me?') When you have your first answer (for example, 'It's a treat'), repeat the question in relation to that statement ('What does a treat do for you?). Repeat the question again and so on. Keep exploring your answers until you reach a point where you can see what your relationship with food is really all about. You might well find that there is a deep-rooted feeling at the heart of your behaviour. Food frequently meets our need for comfort on some level.

There is a worked example of this activity on my website: www.jessicarobbins.co.uk.

The word-association game

It's good to know if you have any negative feelings associated with being slim. If you've ever used phrases such as 'skinny bitch', then you do! Your subconscious mind may not allow you to view yourself as a bitch, so it would sabotage your efforts to lose weight to protect you from becoming one.

1 *Think of the size, shape or weight you want to be and what that size represents to you. Think of the word that you would use to describe the size or shape you want to be. For example, 'slim'.*

2 *Now think about the words you tend to associate with that size – attractive, skinny, bitch, small, pathetic, weak, petite, etc. Keep freely associating until you can't think of any more words.*

3 *What do the words in question 2 mean to you? Are there many words in the list that are negative (that is, words you would not like to associate with your own identity)?*

4 *If the meanings were all neutral or positive, congratulations: your subconscious mind will view your desired size as a positive step. If the meanings were sometimes negative, your subconscious mind might resist helping you to achieve a goal that associates you with those negative descriptions.*

5 *Now do the same exercise again, but associate the word in question 1 with only positive words. This builds up a representation of how you want to be and makes you feel enthusiastic about reaching your goal. For example, slim,* *lean, strong, toned, muscular, bold, leopard, panther, lithe, smooth, sleek, elegant, beautiful.*

Thought forensics – find the suspect

To get to the root of some of your unwanted habits, this great exercise investigates what happened after you've acted on a bad habit – a bit like a detective investigating a crime scene. What we want is a motive, an opportunity and a suspect. It was this exercise that showed me that I always overate in response to being disappointed. Ask yourself the following questions:

- *What was the incident – the unwanted behaviour? For instance, you bought a loaf of bread and ate it on the way home.*
- *What were your thoughts after the incident?*
- *What were your thoughts during the incident?*
- *What were your thoughts just before the incident?*
- *What were you saying to yourself?*
- *How did it make you feel?*
- *What did you want to do?*

The suspect is the thought or phrase that triggered the chain of events. Once you've recognised the suspect thought, go to page 151 and change this belief so that it won't trigger unwanted behaviour again.

STAGE 3
GET READY FOR CHANGE

How do you know whether you're in the right frame of mind to bring about change in your life? How do you know what you really want and what is right for you? Before embarking upon any change, it is important to know what you want to achieve. The following brief visualisation exercise will help you to see where you're heading.

Visualise your future

Begin by creating a clear picture in your mind of what your ideal outcome would be. Feel in your body the changes you want to make and the excitement of being able to make them last a lifetime. Decide what would feel perfect for you in your life. As you make the changes, you can let your old beliefs and habits about food just fall away, making room for fresher, healthier ones to grow in their place. Understand that it will be a liberating and empowering experience, and will open up the better life that you deserve.

Begin with the end in mind.

STEPHEN TOVEY, EDUCATOR AND AUTHOR

Have you got a clear picture in your mind now? Do you know what you really want? If you are unsure because you are not used to believing that change is possible, don't worry; be patient with yourself. Simply repeat the visualisation exercise above several times a day until your desires reveal themselves to you.

Why diets fail

Most of us know which foods make us fat and which make us healthy. It isn't knowledge we are short of: the fact is that we tend to focus on the symptoms of the problem instead of the underlying cause. Think how it would feel to try sailing a boat with a hole in it. You might, for a short time, be able to bail quickly enough to prevent the boat filling with water and sinking. However, a longer term and much happier solution would be to fix the hole. Similarly, diets are simply a quick fix that do not address the root cause of the problem. There are three main reasons why diets fail.

1 Being overweight has become part of your identity

When you succeed in losing weight, do you feel that you don't know who you are any more? Do you find that you no longer recognise the person in the mirror, or become uncomfortable about the attention you now receive? Losing weight can threaten major, long-held beliefs about ourselves (for example, 'I can't lose weight, I'm always going to be big, I like my food, I'm big and strong, No one will love me'). Without alternative beliefs to take their place, it can be tempting to return to familiar ground, where we feel more comfortable and safe. Believe it or not, being fat can offer great excuses for avoiding life and missing out on things. When we are overweight we use body shape as the excuse for everything we don't have in life. ('I'll never have a boyfriend; I'm too fat to be noticed.' 'I'll never get a promotion; they'll choose someone slimmer than me.' 'There's no point me joining the race; my weight means that everyone else will be faster than me.') I remember how I felt being overweight. I may have been unhappy and I may have felt powerless, but my weight meant that I could avoid taking responsibility for my life. My weight was something I could conveniently blame for just about everything. That kind of excuse can be hard to give up.

2 You are failing to ensure that your emotional needs are being met

The triggers and behaviours that lead us to overeat are connected to our emotional needs too. Are you under stress? Do you feel lonely? In the absence of someone to hug you or solve your problem for you, do you reach for the chocolate/crisps/ice cream/extra portion? Many of us use food to create a feeling of immediate satisfaction and personal comfort. By contrast, going on a weight-loss diet won't meet those needs. Without an alternative source of immediate comfort, such as the warm company of friends, a physical relationship, the enjoyment of a sport, or shopping, we can abstain from comfort eating for only so long before, like a rubber band, we return sharply to our old eating habits so that our emotional needs can be met once again.

3 You are not developing sustainable habits that will keep weight off after you've lost it

The habits that keep us overeating can be deeply ingrained. We either choose diets that fit around our habits so that they never actually change, or we try to create new habits, but fail to meet our emotional needs (as above). Sustainable habits need to be practised until they are automatic – programmed into your subconscious mind so that you do them literally without thinking. Your choices, of whether to reach for a glass of water, a book, a magazine, or to cuddle with a loved one or a pet, instead of snacking in front of the TV, need to be instant and automatic in order to change the moment of desire and 'see off' the food craving.

4 There could be an hereditary factor

It is thought that some people might have a genetic predisposition to obesity. If you feel this is true of you, it could be that you don't produce or respond to the relevant hormones in your body, so your hunger never feels satisfied. This doesn't mean that you can't lose weight, but it might mean you have to be clever about achieving your goal.

Three rules to help you succeed in changing your body weight

Remember the three requirements for success that were outlined in the introduction?

1 Redefine your identity and the beliefs that will help you be who you want to be.

2 Find new empowering ways of meeting your emotional needs so you don't need to 'fill up with food'.

3 Take responsibility: learn to listen to your body and adopt the eating habits of healthy, happy people.

Following these guidelines will help you to eat when you're hungry and stop when you're full. You'll learn to eat what your body tells you it needs and to nourish yourself emotionally. You will find pleasure in moving your body and expanding your horizons.

You can take more exercise and take care of yourself by eating healthy foods. You can also do yourself a favour by ditching the guilt, shame, blame and other negative emotions that might block the part of your brain responsible for shutting off hunger. Work on your self-esteem and help your body chemistry to work for you by giving it the best possible chance of success. You have the power to make a choice to feel good about yourself and be kind to your body. That means keeping positive, patient and not giving up on yourself – ever.

Facts about the causes of weight gain

Knowledge is power – usually. The problem is the weight-loss diet industry is so financially lucrative that all kinds of 'false' knowledge has made its way into common folklore. Contradictory advice over whether you should eat more protein or eat more carbohydrates, whether they should be eaten separately or together, whether to eat more fibre, eat more fruit, watch calories, watch the glycaemic index, and any other more wacky variations. Instead, it is important to realise that there are just three basic facts that will ensure weight loss:

- Eat only when you're hungry.
- Don't eat more than you need.
- Keep your body on the move.

Keep aware of these three basic principles and your path to success will be simple.

Fact: if you eat more than your body can burn off, you will gain weight.

Regardless of your body's metabolic rate or your choice of food, if you are eating more than your body can burn up, you will gain weight. The bottom line is based on the simple equation that calorific input should not exceed energy output, so you've got three things you can do to lose weight:

- Reduce food input so you eat no more than satisfies you.
- Increase energy output so that you are doing more work.
- Ensure the process that turns your food into energy is working efficiently and not trying to conserve your energy for a rainy day. You can help achieve this by eating a healthy and varied diet that is low in saturated fats, salt and sugar.

Fact: if you eat at any time when you're not hungry, you are overeating.

If you are routinely eating for reasons other than hunger, but just can't stop, even though you are storing excess fat, which you know is making you miserable, overeating has become a problem for you. There are many reasons why you might eat when you're not hungry, and it will help you to control your cravings if you take time to recognise your food triggers (see pages 46 and 60). Ask yourself:

- When was the last time your stomach actually rumbled?
- How do you decide when it's time to eat?
- When do you know when to stop eating?

The bottom line here is that if you're not eating directly in response to your natural hunger, you are overeating.

Fact: there's no such thing as a 'fast' metabolism, but you can help it to be more efficient.

Your metabolic rate is the amount of energy used up by your body to keep its systems and muscles alert and moving over time. Metabolism is a chemical process that operates at roughly the same speed all the time. What changes when the metabolism increases is the 'amount' of fuel you burn each

The myth of the 'fast metabolism'

A colleague of mine had always been underweight. He used to tell me he could eat anything he wanted and not put on weight: 'I just have a fast metabolism.' I refused to believe this was true until I'd seen the evidence, so I monitored his eating over a couple of months. It turned out that a lot of the time he forgot to eat, or ate very little. He arrived at work without having eaten breakfast, and would then grab a cup of coffee and a sweet snack. If he remembered to stop for lunch, he'd eat a sandwich and possibly a chocolate bar. Dinner wouldn't be until about 8 p.m., when he would generally eat pasta or fish. His maximum intake was about 1500–2000 calories a day. He might have been thin enough to fill an overweight person with envy, but he wasn't eating enough and was a long way from being in tune with his body. His belief that he could eat anything he wanted was not wrong. He *did* eat anything he wanted; he never restricted himself. He just didn't *want* much food. His weight was nothing to do with his metabolism; it had everything to do with how little he was eating.

day. You can increase the number of calories you burn by taking more exercise, but it will make no difference to the rate at which you burn calories. The most efficient way to boost the number of calories you burn each day is to build more muscle and to keep physically on the move so that more calories are needed to fuel your body and maintain your body strength.

Are you ready for change?

Now that you know why diets fail, and you have the three secrets of weight-loss success, ask yourself 'Am I ready to change?' Are you ready to take a close look at the deep-seated reasons that trigger you to overeat, while accepting the simple, practical things you need to do to lose weight? Once you have committed yourself to this new approach, your decision to change will take on its own momentum – if you let it. You might start to feel on a deep level that these changes are completely intuitive and natural. Your passion and focus will propel you forward towards your goal and your future success.

In order to make change happen, you need first to believe that you're in control. Your commitment to your goal is essential (more about this in Stage 4); you need a burning desire to succeed and a great deal of tenacity. You also need to keep asking yourself the right questions to keep yourself on track. Great questions deliver interesting answers. Great questions (see page 71) will help you to understand why certain foods are a problem for you and how your feelings relate to your overeating. (See page 45 for more about your feelings.)

Change is not a one-off event after which things go back to 'normal' or stay the same. You are *constantly* changing, just as the world around you is changing too. If you learn to accept this and see it as a positive opportunity for ongoing improvement, you can make ongoing changes that will carry you towards the life you want to live and the person you want to be.

Learn to ask quality questions

Stage 1 of the program explained why remaining flexible is an important aspect of inviting positive change into your life. Keeping an open mind includes having the ability to ask questions. Quality questions tend to be open questions that invite positive answers. They will help to change your perspective and encourage new ways of thinking that will help you to change the way you think. On the other hand, if your life is full of negative statements, such as, 'I'm never going to be able to lose weight', your brain will accept this as the truth instead. It won't bother to question your belief, and there will be no change.

Quality questions can be used to reframe rhetorical questions that begin from a negative standpoint. For example, instead of saying, 'What's the point in exercising? I know I'll just give up!' try saying, 'How am I going to lose excess weight and really enjoy the process?' This is an 'open' question that will invite your brain to think creatively and find solutions. Your brain will access its creative powers of thought and give you a quality answer. Quality questions that lead to solutions tend to begin with the word 'how' (see the exercise on page 79).

With great responsibility comes great power

The next step is to realise that, regardless of the events in your life that have brought you to where you are now, you already have the power to create new and positive experiences for yourself – in your subconscious mind. All you need do is turn this awareness into a more *conscious* skill and use it to point you in the direction that you want to go. Using the power of quality questions, the next time you feel irritated or annoyed by something, try asking yourself 'What can I do about it?'

With great power comes great responsibility and, in turn, great responsibility gives you an awesome amount of power and control over your life. If you are driving your life's experiences, it means you are in charge, and can therefore change anything you don't like. If, on the other hand, you feel you have no control and believe you have no responsibility for your life, who do you consider is making the decisions? Does it mean that someone else is to blame for everything that happens to you? Does it mean that your ability to pass your driving test was all down to your instructor, or that passing your exams was due solely to your tutor's hard work? If you want to take responsibility for the good things that happen in your life, you need also to be willing to acknowledge responsibility for the bad and unwanted results too.

Letting go of your legacy

Many of us blame our parents for the way we have turned out as adults. Our reluctance to take responsibility for our actions may stem from being over-protected as children, or punished for the things we did. The fear of 'getting it wrong' or of 'letting people down' can run deep. The voices that warned us, told us off, criticised us or sounded disappointed when we were very young can still be heard loud and clear by the subconscious mind in adulthood. Sometimes we need to tune into the inner voices more clearly to realise where they stem from and to acknowledge that their time has passed.

As adults we are free to hold our own opinions and make our own decisions. Most parents try to give their children a good start in life, but your parents' choices do not have to remain your choices. Now is the time to have the courage to stop the blame game and take responsibility for who you are, who you want to become and how you choose to behave. Your parents are not responsible for your weight gain, because whoever is responsible is also in control. Are your parents in control of your habits and choices now? Thankfully not. You are!

Responsibility is an incredible gift because it gives you such control over your life. The downside is that it can be hard work and, yes, you have to take responsibility and fix things if you screw up! The upside is that by screwing things up you will learn how to do things better in future, and the less scared you are of 'failure' in the future, the stronger you become and the better your life will be.

Making the commitment to change

You never have to feel helpless again if you choose to take conscious responsibility for all your actions. In order to achieve lasting change, you need to be determined and to hold your intention in mind all the time. However, it's quite normal for there to be times when your focus slips. When this happens, revisit the contract you made with yourself (see page 29). Look at my website (www.jessicarobbins.co.uk) where you will find a copy of the contract that you can print off and put on your wall. Read it, believe it and commit to it – every day. Bear in mind your commitment to yourself at all times, and remember that in any situation in life you have three choices of action:

1. To accept your situation or surrender to it.
2. To change your situation or your perspective of it.
3. To remove yourself from the situation.

Choosing any of these responses means that you are taking responsibility and determining your own reaction to the situation. They are the equivalent of the 'fight, flight, or freeze' responses that an animal has when it faces danger. By contrast, the reaction that is the most disempowering is to whine, blame others or wait for someone else to take responsibility for you. By deciding on one of the three positive choices of action, you will always be and feel in control of your life.

How I found my power again

I spent many years in a relationship with a guy who I used to think took my power away and left me feeling powerless and ignored. My feelings became my excuse for overeating and I put on several kilograms in weight. Eventually I came to realise that no one can take your power away; you give it away by choice. It is your own fear that causes you to surrender, but even that fear belongs to you and no one else. In my case, I felt helpless to change his behaviour towards me, so I tried to accept it. I thought about leaving, but feared I would be losing love and risked being all alone and vulnerable. What if no one else could love me? I traded my self-esteem and confidence for his attention, secure in the knowledge that he would never leave me. When I eventually realised it was me who gave my power away, I stood up immediately and took it back. At first I was concerned about the consequences, but the power I felt from taking responsibility for my life and my feelings made it the easiest thing in the world to do. Amazingly, I started to find it easier to take control of my weight too. Once you've learnt that you can rely on yourself no matter what, you know you can achieve whatever you put your mind to – and need never be scared or lonely again.

STAGE 3 ACTION PLAN

In order to bring about positive change, you need to be able to let go of, or come to terms with, your past. The third-stage activities are all about taking control of your life and making sense of your actions and motives. I will be encouraging you to ask yourself good-quality questions that will give you good-quality answers. The more you can expand the power and influence of your own mind, the more self-sufficient you will become. Fear of change makes us hold on to unhelpful habits and behaviours. The more open you are to change, the more easily you will expand your habits and your horizons.

➊ Expand your mind to solve your problems

When trying to solve a problem, we often behave as if we are stuck in a maze. We venture down many false avenues, hoping that each will provide us with the solution we need, often revisiting again and again avenues that we know won't work because we can't see the bigger picture. If we remove ourselves from the maze and look at it from a distance, a new perspective presents itself and the route through it becomes instantly clear and achievable.

Similarly, we need to give ourselves some distance when considering our own life. The brain needs time to absorb information. Taking a pause from thinking about a problem will often allow a new perspective to 'pop up' from nowhere. Suddenly, your solution is staring you in the face. This has probably happened to you when you've been doing a crossword and just can't think of an answer. You put the paper down and get a cup of tea. When you return, you take one look at the question and instantly think of the solution.

The following technique uses this principle to encourage you to find new and helpful insights into your thoughts and behaviour by shifting your focus away from your problem and allowing your brain to come up with new understandings and insights.

Work with a partner (or on your own) and ask him or her to alternate between asking you to describe the problem (how it makes you feel, how it affects you, what form it takes, and so on) and then asking you to describe either:

a) *A time when you achieved something, solved a problem or were really happy, or*
b) *Any memory that pops into your mind.*

Using a) will help your mind to find solutions to your problem, and using b) will help you gain insights into your current problem. So:

- *Describe your problem. (This usually takes 1–2 minutes.)*
- *Describe a) or b). (You might repeat yourself, or find something unexpected pops into your mind. Go with the flow.)*
- *Describe your problem. (Again, you might repeat yourself or go off on a tangent about how this problem affects another area of your life. There are no firm rules.)*

Continue in this way, repeating and alternating describing a) or b) until you feel you either have a solution, or have found the cause of the problem, or have freed up enough energy to deal with the problem more easily. Even if you don't find a solution instantly, the problem will begin to feel much more manageable. Your partner should avoid entering into conversation with you or commenting on what you're saying. He or she should simply ask alternating questions.

Taking control

This can be a hard task, as it requires you to let go of any blame you might put on other people for the things that have happened in your adult life, and it encourages you to take full responsibility for yourself. It's an exercise designed to empower your life.

1 *Start by considering which areas of your life you would like to change (for example, your weight, your job, your relationship). Whatever they are, whether large or small, list them. Write them all down. And make a note of why you are unhappy with the current situation and how it makes you feel. (For example, I hate being overweight. It makes me feel so unhappy.)*

2 *Now visualise yourself being in total control of your life and try to identify the choices you made that led to each situation occurring. Ask yourself, 'How did I create this situation?' (For example, when my relationship ended I started eating comfort food.)*

3 *Next consider whether you want to accept, change or remove yourself from the situation, and visualise each of the following scenarios:*

- *If you chose to accept the situation, how would you do that?*
- *If you chose to change the situation, how would you do that?*
- *If you chose to remove yourself from the situation, how would you do that?*

4 *Finally, decide which course of action feels like the most appropriate for you to take. Is it also the action that will make you the happiest?*

Knowing that you are the total creator of your universe, now close your eyes and visualise yourself doing what you would like to do, and with life working out just the way you would like it to.

The point is that when you are willing to accept that you are the cause of everything in your life, you can really start to take control of it. Even if you don't think it's true, it is more beneficial to believe you did something on purpose than to believe you are the victim of someone else or circumstance.

For further guidance on how to use this activity, and a worked example, please visit my website (www.jessicarobbins.co.uk).

Learn to ask quality questions

Try asking yourself the following powerful 'how' questions. Feel free to replace any of them with questions that are more relevant to you. When you've asked yourself a new question, brainstorm as many different responses as possible so that you can see just how creative your brain can be. You don't have to agree with the ideas – just see that there are more options than you thought at first.

'How can I make sure that I eat more healthily?'
'How can I divert myself when food cravings hit me?'
'How can I make going to the gym enjoyable?'
'How can I lose weight effectively and enjoy the process?'

Once you have thought of a solution, you can follow up with 'who', 'which' and 'what' questions:

'Who can I phone for a chat instead of comfort eating?'
'Which book shall I read instead of watching television and snacking?'
'What one new thing can I plan for this week that I have never experienced before?'

You may be surprised to see how receptive your brain is to thinking creatively and how ready it is to react positively. Quality questions put you back in control.

STAGE 4
SET YOUR GOALS

Before you can bring about change, you need a realistic picture of where you are now, a clear idea of where you want to go, and a rough idea of how you plan to get there. Your goals are all important because they give you a clear view of the path you are taking, but knowing where you have started from is important too so that you can tell how far you have travelled.

Where do you stand now?

Use the chart overleaf to get an accurate account of your starting point. Take a realistic look at where you are now. The more honest you can be with yourself and the more you can fill in, the better. Once you have something in writing about your current situation, you can change it. It becomes a problem-solving exercise: an adventure with a clear starting point. When you have filled in the chart as thoroughly as you can, put it away somewhere. Focus on moving forward to where you want to be. This will be used to celebrate your improvements and your successes and to show you how amazing you are!

Where do you want your finishing point to be?

If you're not feeling very upbeat after filling in your reality chart, just remember that 'seeing it the way it is' hasn't made anything worse. All that's changed is that the facts have now been written down so you can't ignore them – and that's fabulous. You can now move forward to whatever state you prefer, and this moment will become a distant memory.

Your reality chart

Medical status

- Are you underweight / healthy / overweight / clinically obese / morbidly obese?

Your GP can help provide you with this information and will help you to decide on some healthy and realistic weight-loss and fitness targets.

Your cholesterol levels: HDL ('good' cholesterol): __________

LDL ('bad' cholesterol): __________

Weight in kg: __________ or in stones/lb: __________

Height in cm: __________ or in feet/inches: __________

Body Mass Index (BMI): __________

Blood pressure: __________

Resting heart rate: __________

Are there any current risks to your health?

____

____

____

Other illnesses/symptoms, whether related to your weight or not.

____

____

____

Are you taking any regular medication?

____

____

____

Exercise level

- What is your exercise level? Heavy/moderate/regular/infrequent/rare/none
- How many minutes do you walk per day? (The ideal is 30 minutes per day.)
- How many minutes of cardiovascular (heart-raising) exercise do you do per week?
- Do you climb escalators? Yes/sometimes/no
- Do you take the stairs instead of the lift? Yes/sometimes/no
- Do you walk to the shops instead of taking the car? Yes/sometimes/no
- Do your leisure activities raise your heart rate? Yes/sometimes/no

Body shape

When you look in the mirror, what shape do you think you see?
Draw an outline of it now.

Waist measurement cm or inches

Hip measurement cm or inches

Bust measurement cm or inches

Blouse/shirt size

Skirt size

Trouser size

Do you have a current photograph? Keep it with this information as an important 'before' picture.
Now revisit the pledge you made at the end of Stage 1 to remind yourself of the power of your commitment to change.

Every step from now on is moving away from this towards something incredible and positive. The power for change comes from spending time planning what we want to create in the future. Ask yourself now:

- How compelling is your future?
- What are you looking forward to?
- What are you working towards?
- What drives you?
- What are you passionate about?

Draw or write down your aspirations and your passions and put them somewhere you can see them easily so that you can remind your subconscious of your goals on a daily basis.

We all feel more energetic when we talk about something we're excited about, whether it's a holiday or a new job. That energy is important because we can use it to channel into the motivation to keep us going and to help solve the problems that we face each day. (See the goal activity on page 95, and 'Identify your powerful purpose' on page 180.)

Harness the energy of passion and let it pull you towards your destiny

If you don't make a decision about what your destiny looks like, someone else will do it for you. If you wait until you are at each crossroads in life before deciding where you are headed, you can't complain if you end up somewhere you don't like.

I have used the following steps for myself and for my clients with great success. They will help you to focus on what you want, to think positively and to harness your enthusiasm. They can be used whenever you are planning and working towards your goals.

Step 1: State your goals in the positive

When I ask the majority of my clients what they want, they tend to give me a long list of what they don't want. We're very good at knowing what we don't want – excellent at it, in fact. 'I don't want to feel like this any more. I don't want to be fat. I don't want to go on looking in the mirror and feeling sad.' But by stating your goals in terms of what you don't want, you will continue to dwell on the things that make you miserable. If you say, 'I don't want to be fat', you will immediately conjure up an image of your body looking fat, and will feel the sense of guilt and shame attached to being this way. Next you will begin to feel helpless about the fact you haven't been able to change. It is impossible to feel positive when you are thinking about all the things you don't want.

Now turn things around and reframe the statements in the positive and in the here and now. Try saying, 'I feel great about myself today.' 'I can look fabulous whatever I weigh, and I feel beautiful.' 'I am losing weight and I am succeeding in reaching my goal.' No matter how fed up you were feeling a moment ago, you can't help but feel better now. Say the words out loud and with enthusiasm. Remember your subconscious brain? It is listening to what you tell it and is hearing you loud and clear. It is impossible to feel negative when everything around you looks and sounds positive. Focusing on what we want gives us a clearer picture of how we're going to achieve our goal.

Step 2: Be specific

In your brain is a section called the reticular activating device (RAD). It filters all the information that is transmitted to your brain via your senses of sight, sound, smell, touch, taste and movement. It 'logs' what is relevant to you and helps direct your behaviour so that you are compelled towards what is relevant. Animals use this device to find food. If their RAD notices something that looks like food, they respond by moving towards the object of focus.

Your own RAD knows what's relevant to you by reading the images you dwell on in your mind – those that are connected with strong emotions. If you are constantly thinking about what you don't want, you are giving your RAD instructions to get more of it for you. Your brain thinks it's helping you. Once you understand this, it is no surprise to find that you are compelled to overeat whenever you think intensely about food or feel bad about yourself.

In order to achieve your goal you need to state clearly what you want to achieve. If you say vaguely, 'I just want to lose weight', the RAD in your brain thinks it has achieved your goal when you lose 1 lb. It is more effective to state clearly 'I want to lose 10 lb in six weeks' time' or 'I want a healthy size 12 body in six weeks' time'.

You have now given your RAD a clear idea of what you want. It will keep comparing the blueprint of what you want with what you're experiencing and, like the autopilot on an aeroplane, will continue to correct your course and drive you towards achieving your goal. Just like using a satellite navigation system, once you have keyed in your postcode you can sit back and enjoy the road. Sometimes during your journey you might travel through some bad neighbourhoods. However, you can rest comfortably in the knowledge that this is the quickest way towards your destination.

Once you start listening to your body, you will begin to feel in your gut (your intuition) whether you are on the right track or not. By focusing with clear intention on your goal you will automatically make any changes that you need to along the way.

Step 3: Be courageous

When you come to set yourself a goal, make sure you aim high. Most of us vastly underestimate what we're capable of and constantly put ourselves down. Invariably, we don't believe that anything we want is achievable, so setting 'realistic' goals at this level would add about as much incentive and belief as you would get by receiving a letter of support from the gas board.

Thinking about your goals should make your tummy tingle with excitement and anticipation. If it is going to take hard work to reach your goal, the result needs to be something really worth going for. Your life reflects the beliefs you have about it. Wouldn't you like to believe that something incredible and satisfying is within your reach rather than simply maintaining the status quo? Which feels better: thinking about achieving the goal that will transform your life, or the one that you feel is realistic? Aim low and you'll never be disappointed. Aim high and anything is possible. It's entirely up to you, but I'd advise you to aim for a goal that sits somewhere between crazy and realistic. Courageous is about right. Your goal has got to be worth your time, attention and effort. You can always work on developing your empowering beliefs to help you there, but you must really *want* to get there – really *go for it*!

Step 4: Align yourself

Achieving a goal is just like any other journey. Consider in advance anything that might be standing in the way of you achieving your goal so that you can plan to break through that barrier. Ensure that you work out any potential issues in advance so that nothing gets in the way of your achievement. It can be useful to answer the following questions:

1. What will happen if I achieve my goal?
2. What will happen if I don't achieve my goal?
3. What won't happen if I do achieve my goal?
4. What won't happen if I don't achieve my goal?

If any of these questions brings up an issue that would stop you or make you less motivated to achieve your goal, take a look now at how you could remove that obstacle.

For example, a client who wanted to be a size 10 had an interesting result for number 4: 'What won't happen if I don't achieve my goal?'

'If I don't achieve my goal, I won't be a size 10.'
'If I don't achieve my goal, I won't feel confident enough to flirt.'
'If I don't achieve my goal, I won't go on holiday.'
'If I don't achieve my goal, I won't have to be on a diet.'

Not achieving her goal meant she wouldn't have to start her diet. At the time she was convinced that in order to lose weight she had to starve herself, so she had a negative association with that. Therefore she wasn't fully aligned with her goal. Part of her wanted to fail so that she could go back to eating whatever she wanted. Luckily, I then told her that with the Jess Robbins' approach, she could lose weight without dieting and eat whatever she wanted. With that belief in place, her goals and beliefs became fully aligned!

Step 5: Visualise yourself achieving your goals

In order to help your RAD recognise your goal, you need to give it a clear picture of what you're trying to achieve. Imagine what your life will look like and feel like at the moment you achieve your goal. Visualise the difference between where you are now and where you want to be. When you visualise your future, you can make it compelling by creating an image in your mind that is big, expansive, colourful and appealing. By visualising and feeling what life feels like when you are at your ideal weight, you can become more certain about where you are heading. You might feel as if you will have to change your personality slightly, or even a lot. Hold in your mind the belief that 'I can achieve what I want' and notice how the visualisation strengthens as you concentrate on this empowering belief.

If you can imagine it, you can achieve it. If you can dream it, you can become it.

WILLIAM ARTHUR WARD, EDUCATOR AND MOTIVATOR

Another benefit of visualising and stepping into the world of your slim future self is that you can ask yourself questions about how your future self behaves in order to help you achieve it more quickly. Believe it or not, the human mind is capable of understanding far more than we give it credit for, so if you imagine something is true and then ask yourself questions about what you're imagining, you will know the answers! (See the visualisation activity on page 94.)

Tips for powerful visualisation

- Focus on the feelings, as they are the most powerful aspect of the goal.
- Add movement to your visualisation. Play a video clip of your goal state in your mind.
- Add a favourite song that elicits the same emotion that you feel when you achieve it, such as motivation, confidence, power, etc.

Step 6: Take action

As wonderful as it would be to make our dreams a reality just by planning and thinking about them, there does have to be the intention to take action. I have seen some truly amazing achievements in my time, and many of them had underlying common factors: a commitment to taking action; a determination that wouldn't give in; and a deep and burning passion to succeed. There is nothing wrong with wanting something. It gives you the courage to try it and the strength to pick yourself up and dust yourself down after a fall. Do not underestimate the power of wanting something. Do not let the fear of disappointment or failure keep you from going after something you want. Nothing is more disappointing than realising you could have had something if you'd reached a little further, and nothing is sadder than regret. The road to success can be hard going at times. However, success lies just a few metres from where most people give up hope and concede defeat. All it takes is a single step to get started.

STAGE 4 ACTION PLAN

Your goals represent the fulfilment of your dreams and your deepest desires. To get to where you want to be you need to have an understanding of where you are now in relation to where you have been and where you are headed. The Stage 4 activities are about focusing on and fulfilling your chosen destiny. Visualisation is the key to creating the future you want for yourself, together with stating your intentions and taking a leap of faith as you ground your beliefs in a time-frame. Once you know where you are headed, nothing can stop you taking action and achieving anything you choose.

Guarantee your goals

Write a list of goals that you would love to achieve in your lifetime. Alternatively, draw them as pictures around a clock face, or arrange them in a way you find most enjoyable.

- *Put a rough time limit on these goals, such as one year, five years, etc.*
- *Now think about three true beliefs that you hold with 100 per cent certainty, such as: 'The sun will rise tomorrow', 'I am reading this book' and 'Trees have bark'. Hold each belief in your mind and notice how it looks, sounds and feels. (Alternatively or as well, look at something you feel certain about. Nature, for example, has a wonderful effect of inducing feelings of calmness and certainty. Look at a tree and think how certain you are that the tree is strong.)*
- *Now clench your fist at the same time as you feel this certainty in order to associate the action with the feeling.*
- *Now double that feeling of certainty and clench your fist a little harder. You may notice your body becomes calm, your breathing becomes deep and you start to feel really good.*

Certainty is a feeling of safety, strength and steadiness. You should always be in this state of certainty when you visualise your goals. Hear what you hear, see what you see, and feel what you feel when you feel really certain and sure.

- *Look again at each of the goals on your list, and visualise your belief that you will achieve each goal by the time you have stated.*
- *Notice how certain or uncertain you feel initially, then clench the same fist as before to elicit that amazing emotional state of certainty.*

In this way the feelings of certainty in your body become linked with achieving your goal. Enjoy the feeling of confidence that you will have your goal by that date. Feel certain of it. Continue to visualise each of your goals in this way every day. The more certain you are of their achievement, the more energy and focus you will direct towards them, and the more you will increase your chances of success.

Visualise being your future self

Imagine that it is a few months from now and you're looking at yourself in the mirror. Your body is slimmer, fitter, healthier and toned. Imagine what your smooth, toned skin will feel like, and what exercise or sport you might enjoy doing to take care of this body.

- *What food do you feed it and how much?*
- *How do you deal with all the additional attention you receive?*
- *How do you deal with your emotions?*
- *Watch yourself go about your daily chores and go to work.*
- *How do you behave with other people now?*

- *How is life different for you and why?*
- *How do you relax? How do you have fun?*
- *Is there anything about this body that doesn't feel good? Something that could potentially cause you to sabotage your efforts? If so, what can you do to overcome this issue?*

See yourself having dealt with this issue somehow and feeling great, and then ask yourself what you needed to change. When you've asked your future, slim self everything you want to know, guide yourself back into the room you're in.

Achieve your target weight loss

Now that you have programmed your mind to focus its attention, you are ready for action. Look back at the charts you completed on pages 85–5. That is your starting point. Now it's time to decide on your goals and to choose how far you will go to achieve them.

1 *What exactly do you want to achieve? Clearly state your intention.*
2 *By when do you want to achieve it?*
3 *What won't happen if you don't get it?*
4 *Any negative consequences to achieving your goal?*
5 *Any positive consequences to not achieving this goal?*
6 *How will you know when you have it? Describe the feelings, sensations, pictures, sounds and so on.*
7 *Is the visualisation of achieving your goal compelling? How many times a day could you think about it?*
8 *What action could you take in the next 24 hours to start you on your way?*
9 *How will you ensure your attention is free for this task?*

STAGE 5
LISTEN TO YOUR BODY

Before I was 27 years old I didn't understand how to lose weight. I imagined that dieting was the only route to success, but I was wrong. I learnt much later that the key to weight loss is to tune in to your body and listen to what it really needs.

I think back to all the diets I ever went on and all the misery I went through, and am still saddened that I didn't notice the answers staring me in the face. The behaviours I needed to adopt were already in the minds of those who were slim, healthy and happy. I just needed to find out what those behaviours were. A word of caution at this point, however. You can't just adopt the one or two habits that suit you. They work together as a network and you'll need all of them if you're going to change your behaviour and 'live slim'.

Modelling behaviour

Over the millennia that human beings have existed they have evolved an ability to pass on skills and know-how to others by watching, mimicking and learning through practice. It therefore makes sense that if you want to be able to do anything excellently, you need to find someone who is already doing it excellently so that you can 'do what they do'. Did you have a role model as you were growing up? Someone whose image, personality and behaviour you admired? Did you try to copy them in some way – their clothes, their hair, the way they talked perhaps, or their ideals and beliefs? Modelling behaviour is an advanced variation of the same idea. Modelling strategies involve not only how someone approaches and performs a task, but also the thoughts and beliefs they have about themselves and the task as well.

Comfort food

Does the following scenario sound familiar? This was me, thinking to myself in a coffee shop, when I still weighed 16 stone (100 kg) and hadn't yet learnt to hear what my body was really saying:

'Hmm, those cakes look delicious. Now what do I want to eat? Well, I want the hot chocolate with cream and marshmallows, but that's far too fattening. Perhaps I should have a herb tea and a teacake. But then again, it's been a hard week ...'

'Can I take your order, madam?'

'Yes, please. I'll have a large hot chocolate with cream, and a piece of chocolate cake to go. Thanks!'

I thought I was choosing food to satiate my hunger, but I was really associating chocolate with finding comfort, to soothe my feelings.

By adopting a successful person's beliefs, strategies, values and language you can start to achieve their levels of success more rapidly. If you want to be slim, it makes total sense to find someone who is already maintaining their weight well and healthily and to model their habits to achieve the same results. Eventually these behaviours will become *your* new habits and you will become just as successful as they are. You might also find that you begin to design a new strategy of your own that works best for you. If you allow yourself the freedom to choose what's right for you and the space to adopt an entirely new attitude or behaviour, this new strategy has every chance of success.

Warning

Beware of modelling someone who has gone to dieting extremes, no matter how prominently they feature in the public eye. For example, aspiring to 'Size 0' is not a healthy choice – it is a fast route to an eating disorder. Far from making you look beautiful and elegant, it makes you look ill, weak and desperate. Work on ways to improve your self-esteem and you'll ensure that you never hurt yourself like that in order to get your needs met.

What are habits?

Habits are learned behaviours that we develop to fulfil our basic human needs (see page 35). Rather like instincts, they are essentially a survival mechanism that enables us to respond automatically, without conscious thought, to protect ourselves in familiar situations. For example, you enter a house through a low doorway and bump your head. The next time you come in, you pause just before you hit your head, and then you duck. By the third or fourth entry, you duck your head automatically, without even realising you have done so. A habit has been formed to help you avoid pain. Our survival as a species has depended on this 'pass or fail' system. In the wild, if you develop a behaviour that fails, you die. If it's successful, you will live and pass it on so that your offspring have a better chance of survival.

Habitual behaviours form pathways in your nervous system like pathways through a forest. The more ingrained the habit, the clearer the path. In order to change an unwanted habit (such as overeating), you have two options. You can either leave the existing path to grow over by not walking down it (for example, by going on a strict diet) or, better still, you can choose to blaze a new trail through the forest (for example, by choosing a new, healthy and social lifestyle that will fulfil your emotional and physical needs).

If overeating has been a habit, there will be specific things that compel you to eat when you're not hungry (see 'Problematic associations' on page 42). A habit is like a chain of events that your subconscious mind has learnt to put together in a specific order. For example, you read a letter about an overdue bill and instantly it makes you feel uncertain about how you will pay it. Perhaps you have a thought such as 'How will I cope with this?' This thought could be the first link in the chain. Your brain interprets this as if one of its basic needs is being threatened (see page 38). If you feel uncertain, you will be driven to find certainty. The brain refers to previous experiences that were associated with dealing with this type of uncertainty in the past. Having found a like experience, it goes to the next link in the chain. The response from one person might be, 'Ignore it' or 'Put the television on'; another might suggest, 'Phone them and deal with it' or 'Just pay it'. For many others, the link in the chain might be 'Eat something'. The more times you have followed the links in the chain to the same point, the more you will reinforce the behaviour and the stronger the links will be. Once it becomes ingrained, the behaviour becomes a habit.

Our habits are designed to help us feel safe and to ensure we do what we need to compulsively to meet our human needs. As explained in Stage 2, habits are useful because they mean we don't have to think about everything consciously and they speed up our response time. Once things become a habit, you can relax and do other things at the same time.

You can see why many people have a habit of fulfilling their need for certainty (control) with food. We have complete control over food, so it makes us feel safe. We can be certain about what we want to eat, where to get it, how to cook it, how much and when to eat it, and we know for sure how it will make us feel. When situations in your life seem stressful and difficult to deal with, this is one area where we can feel in charge.

However, habits can be changed, and you will find that these new habits ensure you keep control over food, but in a much more positive and healthy way. We can feel completely certain about the taste of food, its texture, how we cook it, how much of it we want and how it will make us feel. We can also make choices about when, where, how to eat it and who with.

Six ways to lose weight without dieting

I have spent time monitoring the eating behaviour of people who appear to be naturally slim and healthy. The results are surprising and I invite you to try them. On the following pages are the six new eating habits that will transform your relationship with food and with yourself.

Habit 1: Eat what your body asks for

Slim people who say they can eat anything they want to without putting on weight often do just that. They truly do feel a complete freedom in their choices of foods. However, even though most of them include fast food, chocolate and suchlike in their diet, on investigation I have discovered that many people have a very inaccurate picture of the *amount* of food they eat, often consuming much less than they think they do, and even forgetting to eat for long periods.

Some people immensely exaggerate the amount they have eaten, almost as if they wished they had been able to eat as much as they said they had! (This suggests that when they were young children they had to develop a successful strategy to convince Mum or Dad that they had eaten loads of food so they could leave the table to play.) Food is not the main focus of their attention, though they often thoroughly enjoy eating it. Enjoyment is more likely to be focused around the quality or type of food rather than the quantity.

Habit 1 in action

When I first adopted this strategy I had great difficulty letting go of my old thought habits. I had always believed that in order to lose weight, I had to eat nothing but lettuce leaves. Surely if I were to eat what I *wanted* to eat, I'd be eating biscuit sandwiches or chocolate casseroles, leading to an even greater calorie consumption than ever. I'd be sure to pile on the weight! In fact, the opposite turned out to be true.

The problem is that when you don't have the foods you really want to eat, you don't feel satisfied, even when your stomach is fit to burst, so you will continue to eat until you have the favoured food. A meal of steamed broccoli might fill my stomach, but I would continue to crave more food because I still wasn't satisfied. This would send me running to the fridge again, but since I knew I shouldn't eat what I really wanted, I ate something else instead, which didn't satisfy me and so on, until I had eaten many more calories in total than if I'd just eaten what I'd wanted in the first place.

Once I started asking my body what it fancied, it began to request fresh salads and vegetables, fish and sometimes red meat, instead of asking for chocolate cake at every meal. Even when it did request chocolate, it needed only the smallest amount to feel satisfied. It surprised me that my body instinctively knew to ask for a balanced diet!

What I discovered is that once you allow yourself this freedom, the novelty wears off and once-forbidden foods become quite dull. Your body knows what nutrients it needs and remembers the tastes associated with these nutrients. It will then send cravings to you to provide the tastes associated with those foods. It will instinctively crave a balanced diet. At first, even if you do eat cake for breakfast, lunch and dinner, you'll soon be craving fresh salads, and if you follow the rest of the habits below, you'll still be OK. You'll be happier because you ate what you wanted and won't feel the need to snack between meals. I dreamt of being the kind of person who could have a chocolate bar in the fridge and leave it there for days without thinking about it or eating it. Now I know I can have it if I really want it, I'll leave it there. The point is that it doesn't matter what you eat as long as you don't eat *more* than you need. You just need to focus on becoming properly tuned in to what your body is telling you (see page 147).

Habit 2: Eat when your stomach is empty

When I took the time to compare my eating habits with those of slimmer people I discovered that my pattern was to eat because I was 'supposed to', or because the moment dictated that it was convenient to do so, rather than because I was hungry. I discovered that I ate pre-emptively so that I never experienced hunger. Rather than eating *in response to* hunger, the sound of hunger for me was a loud brass band that went off in my head. The thought of being hungry was frightening because I believed that if I got too hungry, I'd panic, and eat far too much of whatever was available. It was a revelation to me to discover that some people become so distracted by other things that they don't even notice when they are hungry. In contrast to my brass band, they barely heard a penny whistle!

When healthy people remark that they're ravenous, their words are rarely followed by a rush to the kitchen. It's more a statement of fact. One of my colleagues told me that even if he was a bit hungry when he got home, he would occupy himself doing other things before he started cooking. He rarely picked or snacked while cooking. Sometimes, if he was busy, he would stave off hunger pangs by snacking on tomatoes or cucumber, and then felt that he had eaten 'loads'. For such people, hunger pangs do not represent a crisis situation where food is the overwhelming need. They are simply a signal that they will need to eat soon. Their association with hunger says, 'If there's food nearby, my needs are already or easily met', so they feel no sense of desperation to eat.

It follows that your difficulties with weight will relate to how sensitive you are to hunger. If you feel hunger but are completely detached from it both emotionally and physically, you are likely to be underweight. If you feel hunger and emotionally and physically overreact to it, you will be overweight. The best solution, therefore, is to tune in to your hunger: eat when you are hungry, eat slowly, and stop eating when you feel satisfied. In order to achieve this, you might need to work

Tune in to your hunger

Remember that the need to eat stems from both a primitive instinct and a biological necessity. The only way your body can check that there is enough food available for survival is to call for food. If you ignore the call for food, your body will believe food is in short supply and your metabolism will slow down. It will *stop* burning as much energy because it needs to help you stay alive until more food becomes available. This metabolic slow-down is the equivalent of going into hibernation. Your metabolism falls by 40 per cent after 12 hours of not eating. (This is why it is so important to eat breakfast after a night's sleep. It doesn't necessarily have to be a big breakfast. Anything you eat will break the fast and get your body systems moving.)

The following 10-level scale shows how the gradual onset of hunger and fullness will feel to your body:

The hunger scale

1 Stuffed and in pain
2 Very uncomfortably full
3 Uncomfortably full
4 Full
5 Pleasantly satisfied
6 Comfortable/neutral
7 Slightly hungry/empty
8 Distracted by hunger
9 Desperately hungry
10 Faint or light-headed

You should aim to eat when you get to the 'neutral' or 'slightly hungry' levels, otherwise, by the time you reach level 8, you will be so hungry that hunger hormones will be released, which will encourage you to overeat because your body has begun to believe that food may be unavailable.

on changing your emotional relationship with food (see Stage 2). It is also useful to understand the different stages of hunger. If you understand where your feelings are on the hunger scale, you will be able to assess more accurately when you should eat. (Visit my website for more information on healthy eating and food cravings.)

Habit 2 in action

If you are in a situation where there are set meal breaks, so you are encouraged to eat at certain times whether you are hungry or not, consider this: eat an early breakfast – at least four hours before the set lunch break. You should then be hungry enough for lunch, somewhere between 'comfortable' and 'distracted by hunger' (levels 6–8) on the hunger scale. Aim not to snack unless you go past level 8 on the scale, but if you have to, eat just a small snack that will take you back to 'comfortable'. This will allow your hunger to build up again by dinner time.

Part of getting to know yourself and your body will be in learning what kind of foods keep you at levels 4 or 5 (full up for longer) and being able to judge how much to eat during a meal to get you to 5 (pleasantly satisfied) on the scale.

Habit 3: Eat until you are pleasantly satisfied, then stop

One of the turning points in my awareness of my relationship with food happened when I cooked an apple crumble for pudding for myself and a naturally slim friend. Although we'd each eaten a generous portion, there was still a lot left. Throughout the evening I kept sneaking into the kitchen to eat further spoonfuls of it. I was amazed that my friend did not seem to hear its siren-like call enticing her to eat more; so I asked her why, if she'd enjoyed it as much as she said she had, she wouldn't want more. The look on her face was confused and her remark was brief: 'Why would I? I'm full.'

My friend, like many people slimmer than I was at the time, always served herself the portion size she wanted rather than dividing the full amount she had cooked by the number of people eating. Whereas I would always divide everything into equal portions regardless of hunger, she left the excess in the pan. I would start eating with the objective to finish my plate, whereas if she couldn't manage it all, she would leave food on her plate. This difference in approach made it quite clear to me that my emotional relationship with food was at the heart of my weight problems. I was incapable of leaving food untouched on my plate. I was programmed to eat everything even if I was full. My objective was different from my friend's.

Other people have different strategies. I have known someone to throw a paper napkin on to her plate to stop her from overfilling herself with roast potatoes. Her fondness for roast dinners related back to childhood and was a form of emotional eating. When I asked her whether she was worried that by stopping too soon she might get hungry again too quickly, she replied logically that it didn't worry her because she knew that if she got hungry later she would just eat something else. This might seem an obvious statement to someone who has no difficulty with food, but to someone who is a compulsive overeater, the idea that it is possible to have that degree of control can be a revelation. Rest assured that as long as you stop when you're pleasantly full, you just have to wait until your stomach is empty again and you can eat something else.

This same friend would also stop eating her main course well before she was full so that she would have room for dessert. In my experience, if you were full, you waited for your main course to go down and had your dessert later, the net result being that you could cram in a lot more food in total. It was revealing to see life and food from others' perspectives.

Habit 3 in action

To summarise: if you feel hungry, eat something and then stop when you've had enough (level 4 or 5 on the hunger scale). If you want more but feel full, give your body a chance to digest. Wait until your stomach starts rumbling again (level 7 or 8 on the hunger scale) and then you can have more.

Food–emotion diary

Using the chart below, record your current eating habits. Study an average week to start with, or continue until you have revealed all your habits and behaviours around food. What times do you eat? What were you craving? What did you eat? How hungry were you when you started? When did you stop? How fast did you eat? What were your thoughts before/during, and how did that affect what and how you ate?

Time	Food	Hunger scale 1–10	
		start	finish

It takes about 15–20 minutes for your stomach to give the signal to your brain that you're satisfied. It is actually triggered by food entering the small intestine rather than the stomach. It doesn't take very much food to release the hormone that says 'I'm satisfied'. The trouble is that in the rush to eat, many of us have eaten our second helping or even pudding before food reaches the hormone trigger point. We need to slow down the speed of eating in order to feel more satisfied.

Your body weight might be seen as a reflection of your level of sensitivity to your body's signals. If you are able to tune in to your body to the point where you stop eating before or when you feel *just* satisfied (level 5) or when you feel *full* (level 4), you will achieve a slim to healthy body weight;

After filling in the diary you'll see habits you want to change and disrupt, and positive habits you'd like to keep alongside the ones mentioned in this chapter.

To discover the particular thoughts and/or feelings that cause any unwanted behaviours, you can do the 'Thought forensics' exercise on page 60.

Time taken	Thoughts before	Food cravings

Little and often?

Some weight-loss diets recommend eating several small meals per day rather than a few large meals. However, if you eat six small meals a day but are hungry for only three of them, be aware that you are still overeating. Remember, if you eat for any reason other than because you are feeling hungry, you are overeating.

but if you regularly eat until you are *uncomfortably* full (level 3) and often feel fit to burst, or eat when you're not even hungry, you will either become or remain overweight. If you get the desire to eat at a time when your stomach is not asking for food (for example, immediately after you have eaten a large meal), it is likely that you are eating to try to change how you feel. Stages 2 and 6 show you how to change the way you feel and behave around food.

Your body is the expert. It knows when it's warm and when it's cold, when it needs the toilet and when it's tired. Your body also knows when it's hungry and what it physically needs to eat – you just have to let it tell you.

Habit 4: Listen to your body

The systems in the human body have not changed much in over 100,000 years. It knows what it's doing. When we were children we knew exactly how to respond to the signals from our bodies. When we were hungry or lonely we cried and experienced painful emotions; we allowed ourselves to be comforted and then moved on. When we were tired we slept, and when we were happy we laughed. When we were energetic, we moved. Then we got a little older and things changed. We had to conform to other people's schedules for eating, sleeping and playing. We learnt to dissociate (that is, to separate ourselves) from the physical and emotional signals within the body, and started to ignore what it was telling us. Over time we learnt to ignore the pain of hunger, having to eat what we were given, or of being ignored, blamed, punished for not eating, and so on, until we didn't know how to recognise those feelings any more. By the time we are adult and expected to feed ourselves, it's not really surprising that we can't hear our body's internal voice.

Luckily, our body is still sending us the messages. All we have to do is learn to tune into them again.

The fluid approach

Compare your feelings about food with the way you feel about water. When you get thirsty, you have a drink. It feels nice to satisfy your thirst, and when you get really thirsty, you might even find yourself craving a refreshing glass of chilled water. However, once you've had enough water, you don't keep drinking. You stop and wait to get thirsty again. In this way, water is best when you're thirsty, just as food tastes nicer when you're hungry.

Interestingly, people who are out of sync with their feelings might confuse the sensations of thirst and hunger. The next time you fancy 'a little something' to eat, try drinking a glass of water instead. You might find that you are dehydrated rather than hungry.

Habit 4 in action

The simple rules of thumb are as follows. When you're tired, get yourself some sleep. When you're hungry, eat. When you're thirsty, drink. When you're lonely, find a friend. When you're playful, play. When you're energetic, move. If you overdo it one day, give it a rest the next. Being aware of your body allows you to become aware of everything that is around you in more depth. Your world becomes more awake. The Stage 5 exercises will put you right on track.

Habit 5: Eat with a new agenda

This habit is about conscious eating. The more you tune in to your food – how it tastes, how you feel when you eat it and so on – the more you will be able to learn to tell when you are full. If you daydream when you eat, it is difficult to connect with your body and tune in to the signs that say it's had enough. When you don't focus fully on what you're doing, you allow old habits and programming to take over. It is very important that you focus on the food you're eating and be consciously aware as you eat. I can remember what it felt like to be watching TV while eating and to suddenly become aware that I'd eaten everything on my plate. I felt bloated, without the satisfaction of enjoying the food. Sometimes I'd be so distracted that I'd have a second helping before my body had a chance to tell me it was full. Those who have a healthier relationship with food are more likely to sit and talk and enjoy their meals consciously.

Habit 5 in action

Always look at what you're eating and eat it consciously and with focus. Serve yourself a little at a time and eat only

Don't be afraid to share

Those people who have a healthy relationship with food are more able to share their food with others. Do you hide away food or avoid sharing? In my overweight days, if I bought a takeaway with friends, I would pile everything I had ordered on to my plate straight away, whereas they would help themselves to a few spoonfuls at a time. They always offered to share their food with me, whereas I was always scared I wouldn't have enough if I shared, or that someone would steal it from me if I didn't put it on my plate straight away. Take the decision to try sharing your food from now on. You will always have enough, and you will strengthen your friendships too.

the bits you like. Better to eat what satisfies you than to put anything in your body you don't like. Eat slowly and calmly. Chew your food properly so that your saliva has a chance to release enough enzymes to start the digestion of your food. No one is going to steal your food and you are never going to starve! You should aim to retrain your mind to believe that eating a meal is not a life-and-death situation. Instead, it is a peaceful time to spend in contemplation of your physical body, being aware of how it feels and what it needs.

Ask yourself what strategies you use when eating. Do you eat too much because you leave the best until last? Do you hold your body in a particular way so as not to feel full? Relax your body while you eat and learn to breathe into your belly to help you feel full more quickly. To slow yourself down, start by exclaiming at the beginning of a meal, 'Wow, that's a lot of food – I'll never get through it all!' That way you've lowered the expectation of what you might eat and have told your subconscious mind that it's OK to stop eating before the food has all gone.

How I used to eat

I used to eat systematically by saving the parts of the meal I liked the most until the end. This was a strategy developed in childhood, when I used it to motivate myself to keep going and finish my meal. Through observing those who are slim and happy around food I have since discovered that the healthy alternative approaches are to eat what you like and to leave what you don't like. Or, if you are in a situation where you believe that you need to eat everything on your plate, always start with a small portion so that you are guaranteed to be able to finish it.

Habit 6: Broaden your comfort zone

As you read this book, you'll start to notice the personal habits that are keeping you overweight. Chances are that you have a number of seemingly harmless habits that trigger overeating or unfavourable food choices. Individually the habits and impulses might seem innocent, but combined they can have a cumulative and devastating effect on your health.

Weird as it might sound, one way to disrupt bad habits is to start doing almost everything in your life differently. By changing your behaviour you disrupt your memory's associations and many bad habits will begin to fall away naturally. For example, if you start to eat your meal at the table and in silence or in conversation instead of in front of the television, you will probably eat more slowly and eat less.

Your comfort zone is made up of your collection of habits – the things about which you feel safe and certain. The first time you step outside your comfort zone, you will feel uncomfortable and the fear of the unknown can make this anything between slightly and extremely stressful.

A conscious effort must be made to keep changing your habits so that you continually broaden your comfort zone. The broader you can make it, the happier and more confident you will be and the less you will need food to compensate for your anxiety. Your personal awareness will increase too. You'll start to notice the behaviours you have that you no longer need, and as your confidence increases, you can just let those behaviours fall away. It can be great fun to break old habits, and can result in other beneficial life-changing side effects.

How I resigned from the 'clean plate' club

I used to clean my plate every time I sat down to eat, no matter how full I was. One day, just as I realised I was full and yet was about to continue eating, I jumped out of my chair and shouted, 'Hey! Wake up! You're full, you idiot!' and ran around the house screaming. The next time I sat down to eat I was fully alert and aware. At the point where I would normally follow my old habit, my brain remembered the voice and the sudden change in state that it had experienced at that point before, and stopped abruptly. This left me free to choose what I wanted to do next, rather than play out an old behaviour against my will.

Habit 6 in action

Think about the bad habits that you hate to have. Finishing all the food on your plate, for example, or eating when you're not hungry, starving yourself and then bingeing, setting the alarm clock early to go to the gym, only to press the snooze button and go back to sleep. Disrupting old habits is a creative activity that allows you to break the chains that bind you and come up with numerous imaginative ways of shaking off your old patterns of behaviour.

Each bad habit you have is triggered by a thought or feeling that, once started, plays out like a pop song from start to finish. Although the situations in which it is played out may differ, the pattern is the same. For example, if you serve yourself three large spoonfuls of mashed potato, you know as you're doing it that it's more than you need in order to be satisfied. The pattern that starts with a serving that's too large will end with you eating all of it. Afterwards you realise that you have eaten too much and feel bad about it. In fact, the problem started before this, when you made the decision about how much to cook. The problem with habits is that we become robotic, acting out the behaviour often without realising, so the first step in dealing with them is to become aware of what we're doing.

Start observing yourself and your thoughts, noting the ones you don't like and looking a little closer into what's happening in your mind and your body when you react. The way that you mess with your habits is up to you, and you can be as creative and outrageous as you wish. Whatever you do, you need to send a clear message to your nervous system that a new behaviour is going to follow in place of the old one (see pages 40 and 99 for reminders about how this occurs).

Whatever you choose to do to change the pattern, you must disrupt the sequence in which the behaviour normally runs. The next time you go to serve yourself some food, you'll remember what you did last time and either continue to disrupt the old pattern, or lay down a new, sensible one in its place. If the old behaviour still feels quite strong, keep disrupting until you feel free to decide on a better behaviour. Be as imaginative as you can be, as outrageous as you like and have lots of fun messing up your patterns. You might, for example, keep putting your knife and fork down during an interesting discussion, throw your napkin on your plate, or spill water on it. People in restaurants might think you're crazy, but the results are worth it.

How I broadened my personal comfort zone

My own bad habits involved coming home from work and walking straight into the kitchen. I would make myself toast and tea whether I was hungry or not, and then sit on the sofa watching TV until bedtime. To change this habit, I got home and went straight upstairs to have a bath. After that I called my sister and chatted to her, and before I knew it, it was 8 p.m. and I hadn't had a single pang of hunger. The next night I avoided the kitchen, went upstairs, got changed and went for a quick walk around the block and posted some letters. I came back, turned on the computer and wrote some emails. At the same time I noticed that my bad habit of eating late at night after I finished work just disappeared.

When I first started to broaden my comfort zone, it seemed a real effort. I didn't want to go out to new places at weekends; I always wanted to go to the shops, watch TV or go to the cinema – things I knew I would enjoy and that didn't take a lot of mental or physical effort. I started slowly by researching fun things to do at the weekends, and before long I was doing something different every weekend. The pattern continued and led eventually to me starting my own business. The additional time I had meant I was talking to people, learning new things, and creating ideas and following them through. It's amazing what starts happening when you awaken from the trance of an old habit! My website (www.jessicarobbins.co.uk) includes a whole list of creative ways in which you can break free of bad habits and broaden your comfort zone.

Seeing off the excuses

Many excuses are heartfelt, but don't stand up to close scrutiny. The following are three of the most popular:

'But there are starving people around the world.'

This comment makes people feel guilty or ungrateful if they waste food. All I can say is that the moment you buy, cook and serve yourself a portion that is bigger than your need (that is, bigger than your fist), you are wasting that food. Whether it ends up in the bin, the toilet or on your thighs, it's not helping anyone in Africa, Asia or anywhere else, and it's certainly not helping you!

A memorial to the clean plate club

Committed members of the 'clean plate club' have lots of traits in common, many beginning before the food is served.

- Eating everything that is put on the plate.
- Keeping food in the fridge past its sell-by date.
- Eating food about to go off instead of throwing it away.
- Keeping leftovers from every meal.
- Eating your children's leftovers.
- Buying extra food when it's on offer, regardless of need.
- Accepting people's offers of food rather than be rude.

All these behaviours are usually centred on concerns about wastage, gratitude and fear, but in fact they overlook the real reason why you joined the club in the first place.

Remember, you belong to the clean plate club only because of childhood conditioning. Most of us were told to 'eat up or you won't get any pudding'. Had we been told that we could have pudding, but only if we were still hungry after the main course, would we still have eaten everything on our plate? Perhaps, but only when we felt hungry enough.

The truth is that you probably agreed to the rules of the club in order to get your free ticket for pudding, or your free ticket to go and play. Knowing that, does it makes sense to be the adult you are and yet still finishing everything on your plate in order to please Mummy or Daddy? Once you realise that the original reason is no longer relevant to your life, the belief that you have to finish your plate, and the compulsion that follows it, should fall away by themselves.

'Throwing food away is a waste – and a waste of money.'

But how much money have you spent on losing weight over the years? Was it more than the amount you waste on food per year, or less? If you don't want to waste money on food, buy only what you need each day. Another way to look at it is that either you or the bin has to burn off the extra calories – I'd rather the bin had to do it than me.

'I will cause offence if I don't eat what I'm given.'

The next time you realise you're satisfied and do not want any more food, just say, 'No, thanks, I'm full up'. If someone (including you) tries to make you eat when you are full, they are inflicting pain, aren't they? Don't let anyone else tell you when, how or what you should eat. You are fully in charge of your own appetite and choices.

Often, when we get to the root cause of our beliefs like this, the belief itself will disappear. It's hard to continue to behave in the same way when you realise you are reacting like a child. It suddenly feels as though a three-year-old is dictating your behaviour, so you stop and put a more rational belief in its place. The activities on pages 76 and 151 will help you to recognise and overcome self-limiting beliefs. They will help you gain an inspired flash of insight into why you do what you do, or might prompt an interesting memory that will break the habit forever.

STAGE 5 ACTION PLAN

The Stage 5 activities are all about becoming more physically in tune and aware of your body, and how you feel about it. Once your mind and body feel fully connected, you will be better able to love and appreciate yourself for who you really are. At the heart of this chapter are six ways to lose weight without dieting. These new 'habits' can be abbreviated as follows: Eat what you want – when you're hungry – and stop when you're full. Listen to your body – learn to eat consciously – and break free of unwanted habits. This can often be achieved by modelling your behaviour on others' who have succeeded in losing weight and gaining health, but true success comes when you learn to feel comfortable in your own skin.

What do the habits mean to you?

1 *For each of the six habits listed in this chapter, write a few sentences to describe what it means to you and how you will implement it in your life. You can write about where you are now with the habit. Do you practise it, or not at all? Do you think you will find it easy to put into practice? Make it your intention to imagine what each habit might feel like in your life. Then do them for real whenever you're ready. You needn't wait until you finish the book – get stuck in straight away! You could start by mentally rehearsing it to see how it feels. Practise enough times in your mind and it will seem easier to do it for real. The mind does not know the difference between what's real and imagined, so the same habit-forming pathways in the brain will be created.*

2 *Write down a list of the slim people you know. Observe or imagine the behaviours they have that help them to keep*

Person	**Behaviours**

slim. For each behaviour, ask them (or imagine asking them) what they might believe about themselves that leads them to 'live slim'. For example, 'What do you do that helps you to be slim?' 'What belief do you hold about your weight and size?'

3 *For each belief that you discover, take a moment to feel what it might be like to have that belief too. Sit with your eyes closed and really feel what it would be like to have that belief. What does the belief look like? How does it differ from your current beliefs? How would things be different for you if you held this belief as if it were 100 per cent true? You can choose to change to this belief if you want to. Decide what you would need to change in order to adopt this belief. (See also the activities in Stage 6.)*

Learning to feel

Many times we overeat because we're not feeling what's going on in our body. We're either not aware that our stomach is full, or we eat in response to an emotion or feeling we don't know what to do with. Physical awareness extends throughout your whole body and out into your surroundings. If you spend too much time 'in your head', you also spend too much time with your limiting beliefs, your past memories and critical thoughts about yourself or others. Spending too much

Beliefs

______

______

______

______

______

______

time in your head, represses awareness. So the purpose of this exercise is to learn to feel again. First you feel things that are outside you, then you move on to feeling what's going on in your body, and practise until you can just be in your body. Be aware of what's going on with it and inside it, without hearing the criticisms or making any comments about yourself or your environment.

Part 1:

- *Be somewhere safe, take off your shoes and socks, and walk around, feeling everything in your environment with your hands, feet, face and anything else you'd like to use.*
- *Feel the textures of things you normally just glance at. Feel the hardness, the softness, the edges of things, and experience the objects you are touching. You can close your eyes to intensify the experience.*
- *Notice which objects feel nice to touch, pick things up and feel the weight of them. Feel them with your arm and your face, and notice the different sensations.*

After a while, you will notice you are breathing deeply, your mind is still and you feel more profoundly relaxed than you have ever felt. This is what it is like to feel. It may be a while since you were so in touch with your feelings.

Part 2:

- *Be somewhere comfortable, either inside or outdoors. Sit or stand where you are comfortable.*
- *Close your eyes and take three deep breaths. Feel what happens in your body when you breathe. What parts of your body move as well as your chest and belly? Notice all the muscles that are directly or indirectly involved.*
- *Now open your eyes and place one hand on either your left or right foot. Notice what it feels like from your hand's perspective and then from your foot's perspective.*
- *Remove your hand from your foot, close your eyes and feel what your foot feels like without actually touching it. Then feel your hand on your foot without actually touching it.*
- *Then just feel your foot by placing your attention on it.*
- *Repeat this exercise with different parts of your body, progressing upwards until you get to the top of your head. (If you are short of time, do just three parts of your body.) Aim to become great at feeling what's going on in the parts of your body just by placing your attention on them.*
- *Now feel your whole body as one body. Feel what your body feels like from the outside. Then change your perspective so that you're in your body, feeling what it feels.*
- *How do you feel differently about your body when your attention is outside it compared to inside it?*
- *Do the exercise again, but this time imagine you are a beloved pet. Treat your body for a few minutes with the same tenderness, compassion and unconditional love you would give theirs. Enjoy yourself.*

An interesting addition to this exercise is to take an eyeliner pencil and draw over your body. You can write words of love and kindness on your body and leave them on overnight, or under your clothes during the day. Your subconscious mind knows they're there, even if you forget, and those thoughts will be carried around with you for longer. You might notice an increased sense of well-being when you do this.

A fluid approach

Spend the day considering your relationship with water (see page 111). Think about it in relation to the six habits described in this chapter and compare the differences between your relationship with water and your relationship with food. The questions you ask might include:

'Do I have a healthy relationship with water?' (The chances are that you do.)
'Do I have a healthy relationship with water because I practise the six habits?'
'Do I have those habits because I believe I have a healthy relationship with water?'
'How can I change my beliefs about my need for food to be more like my need for water?'

If you think about it, the end result is the same. Your belief is that you have a healthy relationship with water and – hey presto – you do.

- *Consider what beliefs you hold about water.*
- *What effect does it have on your body and how do you know you're right?*
- *How do you know when you've had enough water?*
- *What stops you having more once your thirst has gone?*

- *How thirsty do you get before you decide to have a drink?*
- *Do you carry a bottle around with you all day, or just find some water when you need it?*
- *Do you think you drink more or less water than an average person?*
- *If you don't monitor your water intake, how do you know that you're not drinking too much? What tells you?*

This should give you a great internal model for where you might want to aim to get to in your relationship with food. It fulfils your needs, tastes better when you actually need it, you can have as much of it as you want, and you have no desire to drink too much because there is always an endless supply. You might like to think about this question: 'How does people's relationship with water change whenever a water shortage is threatened?'

STAGE 6
BREAKING THROUGH

This stage is all about getting results. It is about making sure you are in complete alignment with your goal and helping you to break the chains that bind you to where you don't want to be. Imagine you are taking off in a hot-air balloon: you are about to light the gas and cut the ties that are keeping you on the ground, and you will soon be soaring into the sky. The final stage of the book will show you how to navigate, stay on course and enjoy the ride.

You now know how your mind and body work, you understand the connection between them, and you probably have a good idea about what's causing you to be overweight. You know your starting point and where we'd like to get to. You also know about the habits that will make you more successful at becoming and staying slim. All of that is very useful information, but unless you take your first steps towards your goal, you'll never get where you're going.

Your first step is to move out of your comfort zone, and asking questions is a great way of doing this. Is what you're doing right? Is it working? Do you want the outcome enough to keep going? Highlight all the parts of this book that help you, and refer to them in times of need to keep confident and focused on your goal. It must be your definite intention to lose weight. 'Trying' is not an intention. An intention gives you a clear objective on which to focus your attention. It means putting energy of thought behind what you're doing

You are on a journey of personal transformation, and during this period of change you may experience a period of confusion when you're not sure of what you believe. For example, you used to believe you could never lose weight, and now you're not sure. This is something to look forward to, because if you're unsure, it means your old beliefs are starting to shift and break away. It's a shift in the right direction. The next steps are crucial to make certain that you head forwards into the realm of a new belief and therefore new behaviour. This stage gives you the tools you need to break free of the past and catapult yourself into the future.

The road ahead

At the beginning of Stage 5 we looked at what habits are and how they are formed. Habits, like all behaviours, are designed to change one state of being into another. Each state involves physiology (what you do with your body), focus (what images you focus on in your mind) and language (the language or labels you use to describe your experiences). Changing any one of these three elements changes your behaviour. Any behaviour performed frequently enough in the same way will become a habit and will become automatic; likewise, if a behaviour is not repeated frequently the habit is lost.

By acting, thinking and saying something differently from what you would normally do in any particular state, your old habits start to break down. The links in the habit chain get weaker and weaker (see page 99), allowing you the freedom to build up new positive habits in their place. Occasionally you will fall back into old habits, but if you persist with the new, they will eventually become ingrained and overwrite the old ones. Often, just realising the origin of your behaviour can spontaneously release you from its spell. At other times, you need to work on breaking down your habits consciously over a longer period.

The first and most rapid way of changing your experience is 'living in the moment'. You can make problems literally disappear by choosing to live in the present and deal with just what's happening to you now, instead of continually experiencing the pain of the past or the potential pain of the future. Remember that in any one moment you have only three choices of behaviour: to accept it, change it or remove yourself from it. When you accept that, life gets a lot easier.

Reframing is another skill that you can use for life. It incorporates ways to change the way you look at, talk about, or experience a situation, so that something that would normally be annoying or frustrating becomes, from a different perspective, a useful or neutral life experience you're happier to accept.

Living in the moment

Stop reading this book for one minute and then begin reading again. Where were your thoughts directed during your minute? My guess is that they were either about something that has happened in your past, either seconds, days or years ago, or something about the future, like the things you need to get done by tomorrow. It is unlikely that you stayed present in the current moment.

The future is full of 'what ifs' or fantasies about what has yet to come, whereas the past holds the keys to our identity and the way we look at the world we live in. We constantly check the past to find out how to behave in response to situations we're in now – in the present. Most of us think more often about something that has already happened, such as a conversation, or about the future: such as a phone call we might have to make, than we do about the 'now' of our situation. The 'now' is just a means to an end: something we rush through in order to get on to the next thing. Of course, when we get there we'll probably just rush to get somewhere else. How much time do you spend actually present in your own body, in your own time?

If something painful happened in the past, all you need from it is the positive learning experience that it delivered. If something hasn't happened yet, you can't be sure it will happen the way you imagine, so feeling the pain of it is a waste of energy. Once you know this, you can ditch painful thoughts and move on. By spending so much time stuck in the past, many of us become habituated to certain thoughts, which lead always to the same 'bad' feelings. We become almost compelled to find new situations that will cause the same outcomes. The behaviour acts as a self-fulfilling prophecy.

If you tell yourself continually that you are probably going to fail at losing weight, you will start to feel bad. Feeling bad will in turn determine how you behave and the resulting behaviours are ones that lead you to put on weight. Hey presto – you got what you expected and didn't lose weight. Look how powerful you are! Look how easily you can get what you want! Imagine what you could do if you were to focus on something *positive* and believe you could have that instead. Try it right now: tell yourself that you are going to succeed in losing weight. Where has your mind gone? Is it thinking of healthy strategies that you can adopt to make this prophecy come true? It really is that easy to change your future outcomes.

Now is the only time you can spend.

ECKHART TOLLE,
SPIRITUAL TEACHER AND WRITER

Stop reading for another minute and this time take a moment to be completely aware of your own body and immediate surroundings and what is happening in you and to you *right now*. If you notice that your thoughts are wandering towards something that's already happened, or something that may happen in the future, gently guide your mind back to your body and your surroundings. Eventually you will notice and understand that nothing except now can ever exist.

Why spend all your time avoiding the present moment? If you rush through your entire life constantly thinking about where you have to be in 10 minutes, the piece of work you have to give in tomorrow, the bills that need to be paid next month or the size you'll be in one year's time, you could find you've reached the grand age of 80 and haven't spent more than one day in total thinking about *what you're doing right now*. I'm not suggesting that you never think about the bills you have to pay, or the holiday you had last year, but first realise that you're doing it and, second, do it because you're benefiting from it in some way.

If you're drifting away into the past, consider what it is that you need to learn from it, or how you could use it to make *now* more inviting. For example, if you're rushing because you're late, why add to your discomfort by dwelling on the situation? Try to enjoy the journey to your destination and face up to the consequences when you get there.

To live in the moment, remember:

- *The past* governs who you were.
- *Now* governs who you are.
- *The future* is governed by whom you choose to become.

If you never give yourself the freedom to enjoy what you're doing right now, you'll still be living in the future or dwelling on the past even after you've lost weight because that's the habit you have created for yourself.

Reframing

In Stage 4 on goal-setting I talked about transforming negative thoughts into positive ones in order to propel you to success. However, you'll notice something very important when you start finding the good in situations. Other people will stop sympathising with you. Whereas before, they may have felt bad about you having such a hard time, and may have tried to help you feel better, there will now be a silence. This can be a shock to begin with if you are used to getting a lot of attention in this way. Letting people know that you're having difficulty or are fed up is an effective way to get help and attention; however, if you start to become positive, most people will begin to see you as inspirational and start to adopt your attitude to life instead. You may find that they come to you in times of difficulty, rather than the other way around. Making the choice between feeling *good* about everything or feeling *bad* about everything is easy – though you might take a while to adjust to the change in other people's reactions.

States of mind

As already explained, our behaviours help us meet our needs. When our needs are not fulfilled (see page 37) we feel pain, whereas when our needs are fulfilled we experience pleasure. Whichever state we're in determines our behaviour (do we move away from the state, go towards another state that will meet our need, or stay put?) and our behaviours become associated with the states they lead us to. For example, eating leads to pleasure because our physiological needs are met, so our memory creates an association that says eating *equals* pleasure.

Changing states

I'd like to show you how easy it is to change your state of mind. Stop what you are doing and slump down in your chair, look down towards the floor and remember scenes from a really sad film. Remind yourself about all the things in your life that you have to worry about. How are you feeling? The chances are that you are now in a state that you would probably describe as low, sad or depressed.

Next you are going to change your state of mind just by changing your physiology (remember that this, along with focus and language, governs your states – see page 48). Take a deep breath, stand up and look upwards or out of the window towards the sky. Smile at the world and appreciate what you see. At the same time try to keep focused on that sad scene and tell yourself how sad it is. Has that feeling of sadness diminished now? You are likely to find either that your body will want to sit back down to enable you to carry on feeling depressed, or, more positively, different thoughts and phrases that are more hopeful will jump into your mind. You will find it harder to focus on sad thoughts. It really is that easy to change the way you feel.

This phenomenon explains why, just by smiling or changing your posture, you can change from being in a sad state to a more positive one. Your physiology, focus and language want to be in alignment, so if you smile when you feel sad, your thoughts and language will fall in line with the state normally associated with smiling. Knowing how to control your physical and mental state of mind is vital if you're to learn how to control your behaviour. If you want to lose weight, you'll need to know when you are in a state that causes you to overeat and how to change it. By controlling your state of being in a conscious way, you can give your body what it needs emotionally, without it having to resort to using food for comfort. Eventually your new choices of behaviour will become new and positive habits that will take the place of your old habits.

Resourceful states

Our states of mind are the triggers for our behaviours. These can be resourceful or unresourceful. Resourceful states are those that benefit you in some way and lead you to a positive behaviour, whereas an unresourceful state leads to a negative behaviour. Being creative is a resourceful state for many people – including me. I find that creativity allows me to access my creative resources and energises me for the task in hand.

Disappointment can be an unresourceful state, because it will draw you towards focusing on the negative aspects of your life or make you feel that life has been unfair. It takes a lot of energy to get out of such a state. In a situation where you didn't achieve the result you wanted, try focusing on turning your sense of disappointment into a state of determination, which will be more useful to you.

Negative states can still be resourceful states, but it depends how you transform them and what kinds of behaviour you allow them to lead to. For example, disappointment might lead you into a state of anger, which leads you into a state of determination and this leads you to a state of success. Resourceful states tend to feel more energised than unresourceful states.

Facing your gremlins

When we are children, we learn a whole range of rules and behaviours that we are expected to obey and conform to. All these instructions are stored away in our subconscious memory. When you listen closely to the internal dialogue in your mind, you will find that much of what is said comes from other people's thoughts, rather than ones you created for yourself. It is thought that an adult's memory contains over a thousand hours of their own parents' instructions. These memories include all the things they said to you when they were cross, stressed or teasing you. Your memory also includes the voices of others who influenced you in some way too: your teachers, neighbours and grandparents, and even your friends and siblings.

Therefore, much of your internal chatter includes echoes from the past. Much of it will be unhelpful and, more importantly, much of it will *not be true.* Your memories may be distorted because your young mind misunderstood what was being said, or your memory may simply reflect one person's *perception* of what was true.

The thoughts that you hold in your mind that are neither true nor particularly useful can take the form of limiting beliefs (see page 52) or a highly critical voice (something many refer to as a 'gremlin') that tells you how useless you are, how you never succeed at anything, how you should have known what would happen, and so on. These beliefs or criticisms limit your choices of behaviour in some way, leading you to believe that you are less than you are. Sadly, most of us aren't even aware that we have a gremlin sabotaging everything we do or say. Our internal dialogue is so much a part of who we are, that we don't pay any conscious attention to it. Even worse, we blindly follow instructions and feel exactly how the gremlin wants us to feel.

Choosing your inner voice

Imagine that you could choose whose voice you heard in your ear all day. Who would you choose, and what kinds of things they would say? Would you choose an inspirational speaker such as Nelson Mandela, an Olympic gold medallist such as Steve Redgrave, or someone of humility who has brought about great change, such as Mother Teresa? Or would you opt for the harping voice of Cinderella's stepmother? How would your life be different if someone gave you words of encouragement all day every day? How would it feel to hear the words 'You can do it! I have faith in you!' when you are unsure of yourself? Would it change the results you expect to achieve in your life? The reality is that you *can* choose your inner voice. Whether that person sounds like you or someone more famously inspirational is up to you. All the time you're losing weight, wouldn't you prefer someone to tell you how great you're doing and how attractive you look each day, rather than undermining your own success?

Ditching your gremlins

Just as you learnt how to disrupt your previous patterns of behaviour, so too you can choose to ditch your inner gremlin. First you need to be aware of the negative things you say to yourself, since most of them will be subconscious at the moment, and then you can start to reprogram them to be useful. Start by listening to yourself think, and by writing down

How I defeated my gremlin

I used to walk past clothes shops even after I'd lost weight and still hear the voice saying 'Shame you're too fat to wear that' or 'I wish I was skinny enough to wear that.' When I realised that this gremlin was sitting on my shoulder whispering horrible things in my ear, I was horrified. If someone I knew had said those things to me, I'd have told them where they could go, so I began to answer the gremlin back, inside my mind. I would imagine shouting at the top of my voice, 'What the hell would you know? I don't care what you think! Get lost! I'm beautiful and look amazing in anything I wear!' I would then imagine that I had a fairy godmother who punched the gremlin's lights out for me and told me I was wonderful. She also praised me when I chose a positive behaviour (one that I deemed positive, not my 'child's' version) and scolded me if I ever listened to the gremlin. Soon, the voices started to change and they became helpful and encouraging, just like they should be. It's now like having my own motivational coach on my shoulder, instead of an irritating little gremlin.

all the things that you say to yourself. Look at yourself in the mirror and listen to the commentary and all the criticisms your gremlin uses. Weigh yourself or try on clothes in a shop, and again pay attention to and write down your own responses to what you see or do. Writing these things down is useful because it can be difficult to believe that you would say such nonsense to yourself. Seeing it written down in black and white will force you to face reality.

Once you're aware of your negative voice, ask yourself whether the gremlin sounds like anyone you know. If it looked like someone or something, what would it be? Give it a shape and a face and then you've got something tangible to argue with that's outside of yourself. Most crucial is to notice the tone of the gremlin's voice and the way the tone affects how you feel. Imagine how you would react if someone you knew said similar things to you. What would you say in return to their comments? Would you accept their comments in the way you have accepted your gremlin's, or would you want to avoid that person, feeling uncomfortable around someone who would want to make you feel bad? You would probably choose to 'ditch' the friendship – and you can choose to 'ditch your gremlins' too. You can also choose to give them less power.

In future, when you hear something you don't like, try repeating what the gremlin said to you, but change the tone of voice so that it's very high, as if someone's taken a lungful of helium as they speak it back to you. Now that the voice sounds so absurd, does it still have the same power?

The steps involved in ditching your gremlin are:

1 To recognise that you have one (everyone does).

2 To recognise what it says – even the things it says so very quietly.
3 To destroy it – by answering it back, by giving it a face and body, and then imagining something bad happening to it.
4 To replace it immediately with a positive, nurturing voice.

Whatever you do, don't listen to a word the gremlin says unless it's telling you how brilliant you are.

What are you focusing on?

When you look in the mirror, what do you focus on? Your good bits or your bad bits? If what you're focusing on makes you feel bad, change your focus and choose to notice your beauty. Remind yourself that what you've focused on is the first link in the chain of your thoughts and at the heart of your self-esteem. Often when we look at ourselves in the mirror, we pick out all the bits that we hate, and then say something negative that reinforces the effect and makes us feel bad. This automatic thought program has been running for many years. To change it, you need to break the habit chain, in the same way as you are going to ditch your gremlins.

Shout something lovely at yourself, tell yourself how much you have improved, tell yourself how you're going to pamper yourself with a nice relaxing bath – anything to trigger new, positive thoughts and start running a new pattern of behaviour.

There is nothing wrong with giving yourself some constructive criticism and encouragement if your body isn't quite how you want it. However, think about the language you would use if you were talking to someone else. If you

How I learnt to feel good about myself

I used to avoid telling myself that I looked good because I knew that I would lose control over myself and celebrate with food. My inner voice would say, 'Oh well, I deserve a treat if I've lost weight.' As a result, the thought of feeling good about my body actually scared me. I thought that I needed to keep myself under control by telling myself how ugly I still was and by telling myself that I had better stay away from food if I didn't want it to get worse. Threat after threat after threat followed criticism after criticism! Of course, my fears were groundless and based on wrong-thinking. I persevered with banishing my gremlins and changing my inner voice. The more I improved, the better I felt about myself, the less self-conscious I was when I went out, and the more I wanted to experience life instead of sitting at home being 'a fat failure' (as I saw it). Gradually, as the 'feel bad' pattern ran less often in my head, the less I thought about food and eating, and the more weight came off.

were speaking to your best friend or to a child about how they looked, would you focus on their negatives or the positives? How would you phrase your comments? Probably in a very constructive and positive way. Don't you owe yourself the same courtesy? To complete the reprogramming of how you view your body image, do the activity entitled 'Mirror, mirror on the wall' at the end of this stage, which removes the self-criticisms for good.

Learning to use affirmations

A useful way to encourage the brain to adopt new beliefs is to repeat them over and over again in the form of positive *affirmations*. These are constructive 'I am' statements that will replace negative beliefs and encourage the brain to think positively. The more frequently you repeat an affirmation, the more often your mind will look for evidence to support and reinforce it. Soon, you will gather enough evidence to believe it. Once you believe something, it will influence and create your new experiences, which in turn will offer further evidence to support your beliefs. If there is anything you want out of life, now is the time to create a belief that tells

How I changed my beliefs

The first time I tried this, I wrote out a list of beliefs that, if I adopted them, would change my whole life: ridiculously positive ones such as, 'I am a beautiful, inspirational woman', 'I am loved by many people and I honour them by loving myself.' You get the idea. I would walk down the street, reciting them to myself silently as I walked. Of course, I noticed that, as I walked, I was feeling great and I must have been looking happy, as people began to smile at me when they passed. Naturally I smiled back at them, and before you knew it the initial smiles had triggered a whole chain of smiles along the street. People were seeing the people I'd beamed at, and they were smiling at the next person they saw and so on. This made me so delighted that I realised that perhaps I could be inspirational. All I needed was to believe it!

you your goal is easy to achieve. Your positive belief will then demolish the beliefs that say it's not.

The appendix on page 181 contains some suggested affirmations that you might like to try, and the action plan at the end of this chapter contains another exercise on changing and re-creating empowering beliefs. Visit my website for further ideas and make up your own too. I'd love to hear what they are.

How to banish food cravings

If you crave a particular food or foods, it means that the parts of your brain associated with satisfaction and memory are having a conversation. The satisfaction part of the brain asks what it needs to do in order for the body to feel satisfied and the memory says something like, 'Eat cake, because the last time you ate cake, you felt great.' In reality, your body is not asking for cake. It is asking either for one of its basic physiological needs to be met, or for one of its higher needs to be met, at the personal fulfilment level (see page 35). For example, your body may be asking for the chemicals that your body releases when you have fun, enjoy adventure or experience spiritual or mental growth, but since those activities tend to take longer to produce the chemicals, need more personal effort, and in many ways are more emotionally risky, the mind asks for cake instead.

Physiological cravings

Sugar cravings are among the most common, and it is easy to get into a cycle of cravings for sugary foods. When you consume simple carbohydrates (sweets, chocolate, bread, sugar and so on) your body turns them into blood sugar (glucose) very rapidly, which is used by the muscles to produce energy and heat. Any glucose that is not burnt off is converted to fat and stored for later. In response to changes in blood sugar, your pancreas produces insulin, which is a hormone that regulates the level of glucose in your bloodstream. Insulin acts like a sponge, 'soaking up' the excess glucose to prevent damage to blood vessels, and helping the glucose to be absorbed into the cells where it is converted into energy.

If you have too much glucose in your blood (after a particularly heavy meal for instance), extra insulin is produced to try to reduce the blood sugar to safe levels. Insulin does such a good job that your blood sugar levels will then 'slump' and you are left with a blood sugar 'low'. That is the point when you will feel lethargic and your body cries out for something to increase your blood sugar – and that's when the sugar craving will hit. Your body craves more sugar in order to raise your blood sugar back to normal levels. Your body is out of balance and at war with itself. (The long-term danger of this kind of behaviour is an increased risk of diabetes because your insulin receptors are overworking and, over time, will stop regulating blood sugar effectively.)

The best way to stop a sugar-craving cycle is to avoid high-GI or sugar-rich foods for a while (artificial sweetener can also affect blood sugar), as well as large quantities of carbohydrate foods, such as white pasta, white rice or white bread. Once your blood sugar levels 'even out', the cravings should stop.

Next time you are feeling weary and you have an overwhelming craving for something sweet, ask yourself whether low blood sugar could be your problem. If your body is signalling that it wants sleep, but you know you shouldn't be tired, you probably have a sugar imbalance. On the other hand, if you *are* tired, and you ignore this fact, your body will ask for a quick energy boost to keep your systems going. That's why, if you stay up late, you are likely to get the munchies at about 2 a.m. It's obvious when you think about it.

Craving with thirst

Physical cravings are caused by your body requiring particular nutrients to keep it chemically healthy. Cravings can be most severe when you are thirsty, since your mind will get you to behave in any way that results in you drinking some water. If that means eating some food so that you'll wash it down with liquid, it doesn't care. The thirst is satisfied. Alternatively, it might be that you are thirsty and are craving a food that you normally drink lots of liquid with. If so, drink a pint of water and see if the craving passes, or you fancy something healthier once you've done that.

Emotional cravings

Any kind of craving, particularly for unhealthy foods, can be very irritating when you're trying to eat as healthily as possible. The first habit of *How to Lose Weight without Dieting* states that you should 'eat what your body asks for, not what you think you should eat' (see page 101). Cravings for unhealthy foods, however, should be carefully thought about before you satisfy them.

Craving comfort

If you know that you're not genuinely hungry, but you want 'a little something', your craving is more likely to be emotional than nutritional. Consider whether you are craving an emotion that you associate with a particular food (for example, I associate Bakewell tarts and chocolate cake with the comfort of being with my mum when we were together as a family); or whether you are trying to escape from an emotion by using food as a comfort (for example, do you always reach for the chocolate when you are under stress at work?). If you recognise these comfort connections, ask yourself, 'What would need to happen to me right now in order for me to forget all about the food I'm craving?' The answer could be just about anything, but you can be sure that it will be something that gives you the emotional comfort you're craving, which will fulfil the need you're trying to meet.

Craving love

The associations between food and love remain deeply connected throughout life (see page 45). Take another look at the question above. If you discover that in order to stop you eating that bar of chocolate, Brad Pitt (or a similar-looking substitute) would have to turn up on your doorstep and take you in his arms, this indicates a strong desire to feel special and wanted. You are using chocolate to try to meet your needs for love and connection (part of your social needs) and for significance (part of your ego need). You know that no amount of chocolate can make you feel special and wanted, but because you're not meeting your higher-level needs (see page 36), you're aiming to do it with your physiological needs (food, drink, warmth and so on).

Once you realise that this is what is happening, not only will you become more in control of your cravings, it might also give you some clues as to what to do about them in the long run as well. For instance, what is making you feel not-special and not-loved at the moment? What could you do to change that? What do you need to do in order to achieve that? Look again at the section on broadening your comfort zone on page 114, and opposite. Choose to do more than think about it ... take a risk and take action!

Craving security

Avoiding stress, feeling fear, wanting to be looked after, wishing all your problems would go away: all these are symptoms of your basic need for security. The moment something happens that you don't want to deal with, you think about finding something to eat. How many of us find ourselves opening the fridge every five minutes when we are stressed, as if the answer to our problems was hiding behind the broccoli (or in the triple choc ice cream). I never did find the solution there, and eventually you will have to stop looking too. The fridge won't help you find your car keys, pay your bills or make people love you; but realising what is at the root of your craving and choosing to do something about it will.

To summarise: your cravings can be physical or emotional. Most physical cravings for foods you'd prefer not to eat will disappear if you occupy yourself doing something that requires your full attention (such as writing emails, speaking to people, drawing, doing crosswords and so on), or do some physical activity for five minutes or more. For cravings you believe to be emotional, work out what you actually need and calculate a way to get it. Remind yourself that you will not find what you're looking for in food, and you want to eat only because your mind doesn't know what else to do. If you need to treat giving in to cravings as a bad habit that you must break through, go to page 116 and create a fun way to beat the habit. Try the thought forensics activity on page 60 if you need to find out which thought triggered your craving. You can then deal with the thought in an appropriate way, rather than avoiding it by eating.

Broadening your comfort zone

As explained in Stage 5 (see page 116), finding creative and radical ways to break your patterns of behaviour will help you to draw a line under unwanted habits and adopt new ones instead. It will also help you to broaden your interests and your personal comfort zone. When you broaden your comfort zone, your beliefs about the world you live in start to change. In my case, the belief that I couldn't function if I was hungry began to alter as I became more adventurous. Over time I proved to myself that I could cope with more than I thought and that there were more exciting things in the world than food. Ask yourself, how will you know how many fantastic ways there are to meet your needs unless you get out there and experiment with all the different possible activities that life offers?

Anchor your thoughts

If you were given the power to put yourself into a positive state any time you chose, would you choose that for yourself? The truth is that you can adopt any state you wish, at any time you wish, and positive states create more resourceful behaviours. It works like this. Think of a time when you've felt really and truly, blissfully happy. If you haven't experienced one, just use the power of your imagination to create a memory that might happen in the future. Now answer the following questions.

- What happens to *your thoughts* when you feel happy?
- What happens to *your body* when you feel happy?
- What do you tell *your self* when you feel happy?

To ensure that you can elicit positive and resourceful states whenever you wish, it's helpful to associate them with something you can do quickly and easily. Playing your favourite song, for example, makes you *feel* a certain way, and often you'll play that song just because you want to feel that feeling. Similarly, you can train your body so that when you do something specific, like squeeze your fist, you feel a certain feeling. All you have to do is get yourself into the desired state, feel it as intensely as you can and then apply the specific action you want to use as the trigger. The action and the feeling become linked.

STAGE 6 ACTION PLAN

If something you are doing doesn't get you the results you want, change your approach and try again. Your brain has held on to your habits for a long time; you will need to help your subconscious to make the permanent changes necessary for you to break through the habit barrier. Seeing and feeling positive results is both powerful and motivational. The activities in Stage 6 encourage some brave steps on the path to making permanent changes and strengthening your self-belief. A technique that uses 'aversion' therapy is also included. It is a tough but effective technique that is designed to banish unwanted cravings forever.

Change your beliefs

Try this on your own or with a partner (it's more effective with a partner). Allow enough time to answer each question before moving on to the next.

Someone asks you:

- *'What is your problem or limiting belief?'*
- *'When was the very first time you felt this way?'*

Get a sense of who you were the very first time you felt this way. How old were you?

(Imagine you can go back in time to be with the younger you, and watch the original event that led you to feel this way. Watch from behind a screen if that feels safer to you.)

Ask yourself:

- *What is the younger you feeling and thinking?*
- *What did the younger you take from this experience/ event that led to your problem today?*

- *What would have been a more positive learning experience, that you could benefit from today?*

Now send to the younger you all the resources (confidence, insight, maturity, etc.) you needed at the time; all the skills and knowledge that, if you'd had them, would have made it a positive learning experience. See and feel that the younger you now feels better.

Now send to anyone else involved in the experience the resources they needed in order to help them act more positively.

See the original event play out differently now with a more positive outcome.

A worked example is included on my website (www.jessicarobbins.co.uk).

Mirror, mirror on the wall

Be brave and stand in front of a full-length mirror. You can choose a small mirror at first if you need to. If possible, do this exercise with a trusted friend who will be thrilled at the success you have. Look at yourself in the mirror and notice the first thought you have without looking away. If it is in any way negative, say the criticism out loud (name and shame it). Notice what happens to your body language when you say it. Do you stand tall and proud when you say that to yourself?

Now exaggerate and make fun of the criticism. Say it in a silly voice, loudly and with hand gestures if necessary. Don't try to identify with the criticism, just exaggerate and change the voice, the tone and the pitch. Now, deal with the next criticism in the same way, and the next. Do this exercise until you can go a full minute without a judgement or a self-

criticism. If you get one that persists, exaggerate it exactly in the way that you hear it. Don't identify with it, just mimic it as if you were on stage trying to entertain an audience.

If you make only positive comments, congratulations. Keep looking until you either hear a self-criticism or you are satisfied that you are happy with your body image.

Banish cravings

This is a powerful aversion technique used in NLP, which changes how you feel about something by changing the way you hold the image and your sense of it in your mind. It is designed to trigger disgust. Be sure that it's OK not to want to eat the food you're craving before doing this exercise.

1 *Pick something you crave, but don't want to eat. We'll call this the craving.*

2 *Now think of that craving food and see it very clearly in front of you. Imagine holding it in your hand if you can. You're about to take a large bite out of it when suddenly you notice there's a hair on the surface of the food. You look more closely and as your finger and thumb move to brush it away, you realise that it runs all the way through the craving food. Pursing your lips, you grab the end of the hair between your finger and thumb and pull. Slowly you extract the length of hair from the food. Just as you get it halfway out, you pull too hard and it snaps. The end of the hair retreats back into your craving food and disappears from sight. You dig into the food a little way to get it back but you can't find it again.*

3 *As you decide to give up, you notice that where the*

hair retreated into the craving food there is something that appears shiny white. You take the first half of the hair you pulled out and lay it down on top of the craving food, where you can see it. You look closely at the white object and, as you touch it, it begins to wriggle and squirm inside your craving food and, with a sudden lurch, a shiny white maggot flops out of your food and on to your hand. You scream and drop the food and maggot on to the floor, and, as you watch, the other maggots that were hiding unseen inside the food begin to crawl out and over the craving food. The craving food becomes a liquefied mass of maggots, and you suddenly notice that they are giving off a stench that smells a little like sick.

4 *Have you ever smelt vomit? Doesn't it also remind you of the sound of someone being sick? Have you ever noticed that when the smell of vomit hits the back of your nose and throat, it makes you want to be sick yourself? You can feel your stomach start to heave sometimes. Have you ever noticed that? The strange thing about vomit is that once you've associated a food with being sick, you can find it impossible for your mind to let you eat it again. If you've ever had food poisoning, you'll know that the food that poisoned you also poisoned your mind, which will warn you that this food is not to be eaten.*

5 *On a table near you there is another portion of the craving food. How do you feel about the craving now?*

STAGE 7
STAYING ON TRACK

As you read this book, you will be making an subconscious decision that everything will be easy for you and the change will run smoothly. However, sometimes we learn the most about ourselves when things don't run quite so smoothly and it's important to know how to use those times to your advantage and recover from them to become even stronger than before. This chapter explains how to 'stay on track' when you feel success is slipping from your grasp.

Emergency recovery

In the event of an emergency when you feel out of control, remember this: ditch the shame, the guilt and the pain. They have absolutely no use here. Contrary to popular belief, you are not actually out of control when you binge-eat or starve yourself. More often it is a reaction to uncertainty or lack of control in another area of your life that compels you to resort to extreme eating habits. It is when you feel as if you have no control over your life, that food (or the withholding of it) can seem like the only thing you *can* control. Anorexia nervosa and bulimia are extreme versions of this state of mind.

If your brain is compelling you to do what it thinks is the right thing at the time, punishing yourself further is not the answer. That will just lead you to repeat whatever cycle of negative behaviour you are in. Instead, look at what has happened objectively and try to analyse what started the problem. The reason the cycle starts in the first place is because one of your basic emotional needs is not being met. From there you can work out what you need to do differently to get a different result next time. For example, do you recognise the kind of cycle illustrated on page 159?

Reviewing the process

- If it is a while since you embarked on your program and you want to remind yourself of the core principles, head straight to Stage 5 and remind yourself how to 'Listen to your body'. Then review your goals by rereading Stage 4.
- If you have started to lose your excess weight, bravo! If things slow down, or you have trouble adopting any of the habits, turn to Stage 6 in order to break through your limiting beliefs.
- If you self-sabotage (do really well for a while, then everything goes wrong, possibly as a result of your subconsciously making it go wrong), it could be because you have some outdated and unhelpful beliefs that you might not be aware of and that are preventing you from experiencing what you want. For this, see Stage 3: 'Get ready for change', then look through this stage (7) to adopt some emergency recovery techniques.
- Self-sabotage also occurs when you are meeting your human needs through food and don't want to let go of what's fulfilling them; in this case read Stage 2: 'Facing up to food and feelings'.
- If you sabotage after you've reached your goal weight, that would suggest you have an identity issue with being slim, so go to Stage 8: 'Living the transformation'.
- If losing and then regaining weight are habits for you, you might not have made the true connections between your emotional needs and the role of food in your life. In this case, reread Stage 1 to remind yourself that 'anything is possible', and reread Stage 2 as well.

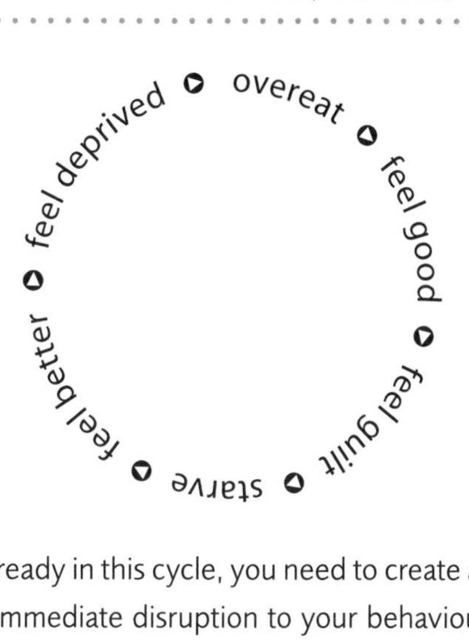

If you are already in this cycle, you need to create a large distraction or immediate disruption to your behaviour in order to get yourself out of it. This can take any form at all, so long as it totally prevents you from continuing the cycle.

Rather than keep yourself under strict control with your diet, follow the habits of naturally slim people and you'll notice that suddenly food loses its novelty. You may go rushing out of your cage of restraint at first, but only because you're used to being shut in. Once you realise the door is open and you can eat whatever you want, whenever you want, the cravings tend to disappear. Food almost becomes boring and this opens the door to fulfilling your needs in better ways.

Face your feelings

If you have had a spate of binge eating and you're off the rails or panicking and don't know what to do, it is vital to talk to someone whom you know will help you. It's time to press the emergency button. Too often I tried to cope with things on my own, too ashamed to ask for help or tell people in case they didn't understand. It delayed my ability to change and reinforced many of my old negative habits. Confide in a friend who will be supportive and help you to break out of the cycle. Alternatively, call a professional who is qualified to deal with emotional issues: perhaps just talking on the phone will help. If your feelings are a mess, you need help to get back on track. Don't jeopardise your future by ignoring your need. Sometimes just knowing there is one person you can call and who will help you is enough to calm things down.

My sincere advice is to find someone who cares about you and ask them to give you a hug. Allow yourself to be vulnerable and express emotion rather than deny your feelings and substitute with food. If you need to cry, cry. It's great therapy and at least you're in touch with what you're feeling. You'll feel so much better afterwards than you ever would from overeating. At least when the crying is over, things seem more relaxed and calm inside you, as if the storm has passed and you can move on. Bingeing is like running from the inevitable, only when you finally release the emotion, you'll feel even worse because of all the extra work you have to do to get back on track.

Put it in writing

Writing things down is a powerful way to make sense of your feelings as well as to accurately record how you feel. Don't censor what you write. Include the part where you're in tears and feeling terrible, as well as the part where you're promising never to do it again. Write yourself a letter at the time you feel the emotion. It makes a big difference.

How I wrote out my feelings

I once wrote a letter at 3 a.m. after I'd been to a 24-hour supermarket and bought and eaten an entire birthday cake plus various other desserts. I didn't enjoy any of it and didn't know why I had felt compelled to do it. I was so afraid of putting on weight, yet I'd been bingeing for days and days. In tears I wrote myself a letter that said, 'Please, please stop what you're doing to me. I am begging you to stop and figure out what else you need to do. You have to find another way because I feel like I'd rather die than feel this pain again. Please don't make me do this again.' Reading it the next day brought back the memory of how bad I'd felt while bingeing, and I knew I couldn't ever do that again. I swore on the life of my family that I wouldn't binge again and I didn't. An oath on my family's life felt like the thing that would stop me, and I used them to help me because I was desperate.

Note: I was scared of putting on weight, but by focusing so totally on 'putting on weight' my RAD (see page 88) understood this as an instruction – 'Put on weight as quickly as you can'! Part of gaining control means letting go of the fear of being overweight.

Choose your own future

When you've been trying to accomplish something without success, you need to change how you're doing it and try again until you succeed. The important thing to ask yourself is what went wrong and to rectify it for next time. The fact that you're reading this book means that you are trying a new way to lose weight and are willing to change your approach. Just remind yourself to keep changing the way you think and feel as well as what you're doing.

You are the only one holding on to your beliefs about who you are and what you do. If you say that you 'always mess up' because you have in the past, then you might as well say, 'I'll always use the potty when I pee.' You are changing all the time and you can choose to be anything and anyone you want. Live in the now.

The thing to remember, if you have an emergency, is that it's just a mistake and you can get yourself back on track. Provided you learn something, you'll be moving forward and making a positive difference for your future. You're making this change so that you can be free of food and the compulsive behaviour surrounding it, and sometimes you need to get it wrong to understand how to do it right. Pick yourself up, dust yourself off and get back to the task of living the life you want to live as the person you want to be. Run yourself a bath, grab this book and do as many of the activities as you can before your toes go crinkly.

STAGE 7 ACTION PLAN

Change and personal transformation are the journey, not the destination. The activities in this section acknowledge that and help you to take stock and re-energise if you feel your progress has stalled. Remember, there is no such thing as 'failure'; every experience offers constructive feedback that you can use to get back on track. The activities here focus on quietening your inner voice of criticism and encourage you to appreciate and pamper yourself. Use the powerful visualisation below to build super-confidence that you can 'tap into' at any point and anywhere – and keep using the previous activities to hone your self-belief and visualisation skills.

The end of criticism

1 *Go somewhere outdoors if possible for this exercise, preferably somewhere picturesque. Indoors will do if there's space.*

2 *Imagine time running along a line. One direction leads to the past, the other into the future. Stand on or beside this imaginary line.*

3 *Turn to face the past and take a step back into it as you state one of the ways you criticise and judge yourself. For example: 'I tell myself I'm fat' or 'I put myself down in front of others so they'll like me.' Take another step and state another way and another way, until you exhaust your list or feel you've reached the beginning of your lifetime on the line.*

4 *Wherever you finish your walk, turn to face the future and imagine that you're the very special fairy godmother of the girl or boy that you were at this age in time. Imagine that you* *now have the very best nurturing skills and you're teaching the younger you how to feel good about her/himself by focusing on the positive aspects of them and their life.*

5 *Now begin to take steps towards the present, and with each step say, 'I am grateful for ...', choosing something to complete the sentence. Alternate with, 'I am...' finishing this sentence with something positive about yourself.*

As you step along the line, back to your starting point, imagine that the younger you is growing up with all these positive messages and feel the difference that makes in your life.

Bubble bath beauty

This activity changed my life! Enjoy a bubble bath, while listening to your favourite song if possible, then relax your body and begin to stare intently at any part that you have labelled 'imperfect' or 'not beautiful'. If you hear yourself label it as anything but perfect, acknowledge it, dismiss it and then continue to stare as if you are waiting for it to do something unexpected, or as if you are looking at the body of someone you love unconditionally and don't mind what they look like. Choose not to walk down the path that the criticism offers you to take. Feel whatever comes up as you do it, but continue to stare. Eventually what you are staring at will become 'just as it is', and when it does you will notice something about it that you hadn't noticed before – something wonderful. Repeat on any part of your body you wish.

Visualise your way to change

Read the following (or ask a friend to read it to you), then close your eyes and do the exercise to install a confidence anchor.

Remember a time when you felt supremely confident, perhaps because you were doing something amazingly well. Be there now and feel how confident you are. When you can start to feel the confidence, make your hand into a fist and squeeze tight. See how amazing you are now and feel the sensations in your body and where they come from. Where do they flow from? Follow them around your body, then double them. Experience that, then double it again. Keep building that feeling of confidence and let it grow more beautiful and more powerful within your body. Squeeze your fist and double it again. See what you see, hear what you hear, say what you say, feel what you feel, and breathe how you breathe, when you're really confident. Make it super-powerful confidence; turn it right up, making it big, bright and colourful. Enjoy that sensation for a moment and then, as you begin to step away from the memory, you can relax your fist and come back to the room.

To test that your confidence anchor is in place, clear your mind and then squeeze your fist. You will instantly feel super-confidence.

Repeat the activity for any resource you would like to anchor and use whatever you like as a trigger. If you use the same fist, you will add a resource to the confidence that's already there. You could anchor 'the feeling of being full up', 'motivation', 'happiness' ... the list is endless. Just replace the word 'confidence' with the word(s) of your choice, and the fist with whatever anchor you wish, such as pressing a knuckle on your hand. However, avoid putting resources from opposite ends of the energy spectrum – motivation and relaxation, for instance – on the same trigger point as they will cancel each other out and give you a neutral feeling.

STAGE 8
LIVING THE TRANSFORMATION

As you start to make personal changes in the way you talk and act, and as you start to slim down there will be knock-on effects in other areas of your life. Your relationships will change most of all, first the one with yourself and then your relationship with others. Spend time getting to know yourself as you begin to change physically and mentally. This new person thinks, feels and acts very differently and believes different things from the old one.

Embracing change

Many of us avoid change. Why? Because we might be forced outside our comfort zone and look stupid. However, you're already changing – constantly. You're not the same person you were five minutes ago, since you're always learning and assimilating new things. How wonderful! Change brings opportunities for something better. If your attitude is one of optimism and positivity, those changes will always bring you challenges that improve your capabilities, make you stronger and more confident and better at the game of life.

It's important you feel comfortable in your body and with the new identity you are creating. Spend five minutes simply staring at yourself in the mirror. Note down any negative thoughts objectively so that you can reframe them and replace them with positive, encouraging thoughts. Praise yourself for the changes you've made so far, as well as the ongoing results.

You might wish to spend some time by yourself, doing the exercises in this book and learning who you are, what you want and how you want your life to be. You'll be spending more time thinking about what you want and need than you did before, and this means you'll be happier and have more energy to give to the people in your life.

You might be surprised to find that not all reactions to the new you are positive. If you make large changes, this can unsettle some people as it forces them to change. Either their perception of you alters, or the way in which they interact with you. Some people will resist acknowledging the changes in you and may make comments that seem negative, or start to behave strangely around you. This may be because your increased confidence is intimidating them or perhaps your achievements have made them feel inferior in relation to their own life.

Aim to learn to accept compliments from others graciously, even though at first they might make you uncomfortable. All you have to say is 'thank you'. You'll get used to it very quickly.

Changes in your personality, such as increased confidence, self-esteem and particularly assertiveness may attract the greatest resistance. Stand up for yourself and remember that the people who love you will be pleased for you, if you're happy and want to share and celebrate your success. Surround yourself with people who allow you to feel good about yourself, and whom you respect and admire. Remember the law of attraction? (See page 116.) Whatever you have the most of you will attract more of, so ensure that your peers' standards are equal to or higher than yours.

When I gained in confidence, I realised that, whatever your personality, you'd always find people who wanted to be your friends. You might be shy, confident, outgoing, introvert, bitchy, bossy, stupid, clever, selfish, generous – it doesn't matter. Just do what makes you happy and other people will feel more at ease around you and then you'll all be happier.

Learning to say 'no'

In my experience, many overweight people have several personality traits that seem to go hand in hand with overeating. It looks like we may all have found the same coping mechanism! A major stumbling block for many is the inability to say 'no' to people and the tendency to put everyone else's needs first or else to withdraw. Not wanting to confront, challenge or upset people is called people-pleasing and that is how I used to behave. You are a people pleaser if you do more for your friends than you do for yourself, you feel constantly stretched by the demands of others, but don't like to say 'no'.

Behind every people-pleasing exterior there is often a huge amount of deep-rooted resentment, anger and fear. If not expressed outwardly, these feelings become directed inwards and then, rather than feel those uncomfortable emotions (God forbid that you should express them in front of anyone) you resist them. You may develop behaviours that further numb those emotions, such as eating, drinking, smoking and drug-taking.

The solution is first to recognise what you're doing, and then to notice how you react to and treat other people. Work out how you interact with them, what you do and how you react, when you don't get the result you want. Once you can see what you are doing, it becomes much easier to become more assertive with people (I don't mean aggressive) and to learn to be honest about how you feel.

It takes practice, but you will eventually find it easy to say 'no' to people. You can help if you want to, but there's no point in saying 'yes' to someone and then regretting it, or being annoyed at them because you resent agreeing to do something you didn't want to do.

Love yourself as you are

Have you ever looked at a picture of yourself when you were thinner than you are now, but can remember that at the time the picture was taken you were feeling really fat? Have you ever stared at that picture and wished that you were as slim as that now? Imagine how it would feel if you could just be happy with the body you have today. How would that change the way you're living your life right now? Do you put things off because you want to wait until you're slimmer? Ask yourself whether it's the 'putting things off' that's causing you to be overweight rather than the other way round.

There is absolutely no point in spending a single minute hating the body you're in. Not only does that send negative messages to your subconscious mind, which manifest themselves in terms of less energy and poorer health, but it's just a total waste of time. You are probably the only person who cares what your body looks or feels like. Everyone else is too busy worrying about their own!

If you just decided to enjoy the body you have, what would you start doing? What would you do that you used to do in the picture? Grab your life with both hands and don't let it go. You can live your life in a prison of insecurity and self-consciousness if you choose to, but that's not really living. Get out there, have some fun with all your lovely wobbly bits, and while you are thinking more positively about yourself and your life, they might just disappear!

Move your beautiful body

It is not essential to exercise in a gym in order to lose weight. I know that the very thought of exercising in a public place, having to wear tight-fitting clothing, and the risk of people watching you can make the whole process seem terrifying. However, the human body was designed to move, and it releases pleasure-inducing chemicals called endorphins and serotonin when you do, so if you *do* choose to move and enjoy your body every day, you will feel very good afterwards!

Brainstorm all the different ways you could bring movement into your life that don't necessarily involve going to the gym, and try each one of them at least once to see if you enjoy it. Find a way to move that makes you feel good about yourself, such as dancing to upbeat music for 15 minutes in your bedroom. It's great fun: I dance in front of the mirror and sing all the time!

If you don't like the idea of exercising alone, you could try sport. Sports make a lot of sense since you're usually having too much fun to notice you're 'exercising'. Healthy competition – and winning – can be a fantastic boost for your confidence and learning a new skill can keep your brain active and alert too. You'll make new friends and it will be a way of socialising as well.

If you are very overweight and find all movement difficult, just start gradually. Think in terms of steps at first and add just a few extra steps daily. Each day it will get easier and you'll be surprised at how quickly you can progress. Every time you move you'll start to feel better physically, sleep better and feel better about yourself, which in turn helps you lose more weight. Remember also that if you can find ways to feel good all the time that don't include food, your brain won't send the message that you're hungry and you'll feel satisfied for longer.

If you do endurance activities, such as running or rowing, your muscles get very good at burning fuel to keep them going. If you do strenuous activities, such as lifting heavy weights, your muscles grow larger, requiring more fuel to sustain them and carry them around.

The joy of sex

The obvious activity that works both as a physical exercise and as a fantastic emotional boost is sex. Your sexual appetite is controlled by the same part of your brain that controls your appetite for food, so ensure you have as much monogamous, safe sex as possible and you'll find the weight much easier to lose. If you're not happy enough with your body to enjoy sex, whether it's because of your physical appearance or the feelings you have about it, do the mind expansion problem-solving exercise (see page 76) and then the exercise to remove some limiting beliefs (see page 151).

Remember that enjoying sex or making love is about sharing an incredibly intimate experience with another human being. If they don't care about your weight, then just enjoy yourself. Don't rob yourself of pleasurable feelings or continue the habit of 'putting off until you're slim what could make you happy today'. Make love as though you're the shape and size you want to be. It's all in your attitude of mind.

Nourishing your amazing machine

I'm hoping that after all your positive self-talk you now believe you deserve to be both slim and healthy. In order to be both you need to consider what you're putting into your body. Instead of regarding food as something you use to control your weight, think of it as nourishment, and a pleasurable way to control your energy levels and your mood. If you put good energy in, great energy comes out. If you feel good, you'll find it easier to deal with life in the way you want to be able to. When you're acting the way that you want to, you'll also be eating just the right amount too and you'll lose weight. When you feel low in energy, your perspective of the world can revert to negative and things can get on top of you, so take care of yourself. When you need to rest, rest, when you want to play, play – and when you need to eat, eat. (The list on page 105 will remind you of the healthy hunger range.)

There are so many ways that you can lose weight and eat healthily at the same time. You could eat organic, vegan, vegetarian, piscatarian (a fish diet), wholefoods, macrobiotic, low GI and low GL (to regulate your blood sugar levels), a diet low in saturated fat ... the list goes on, and there is a wide variety of books on the subject that you can explore at your leisure.

The 80/20 rule is a useful one to remember. It states that 80 per cent of your food should be wholesome, good and natural, and 20 per cent should be purely for pleasure.

What is wholesome, good, natural food? It is food that has not been over processed; food that comes straight from the ground or the grain and is lovingly prepared and cooked by you at home. When I say cooked, I don't mean that you simply pressed buttons on the microwave or opened a can and heated it up.

Drink plenty of water too. You can drink up to 3 litres (6 pints) a day, and this alone will make you feel great. It's better if you sip it slowly throughout the day, but drinking larger amounts, less often, will result in fewer trips to the toilet. To avoid having to get up in the night don't drink too much within two hours of bedtime.

I enjoy whole grains, such as brown rice and quinoa, pulses and lots of fresh, organic vegetables and salads; I drink rice milk or soya milk interchangeably with cow's milk. I also eat chocolate and crisps as and when I please. I have been known to eat pizza and enjoy a bottle of wine with friends. I also like a good cup of freshly ground coffee. I never thought I'd be able to say that I eat anything and everything I want, but I do, and I never make myself feel as if I'm going without. I never eat anything I don't like and don't feel obliged to eat something just because it might upset someone to refuse. Instead, I take time to enjoy the foods that make my body

How I eat now

I have tried and tested many different kinds of healthy diet and the easiest and most pleasurable for me is a mainly vegetarian diet with the addition of fresh fish. No diet I would recommend could ever be strict because as soon as you restrict foods they become emotionally valuable or tantalising. No one food is more emotionally valuable than another, so give yourself permission to eat whatever you want. Once you understand the effects of certain foods on your body and how they make you feel, you can start creating the diet that's right for you based on how great you want to feel.

feel energised and clean, rather than behave like a dustbin for takeaway boxes.

Whatever you do, spend some time discovering the way that good, wholesome food makes you feel. Notice how you don't have as many cravings when you eat natural, cleansing foods. You might have to persevere at first, because if you've eaten a lot of processed foods in the past your taste buds will be used to strong and harsh flavours. Natural foods have gentler, more subtle flavours, but there's nothing subtle about the energy you get from them.

Visit my website (www.jessicarobbins.co.uk) for more detailed information about how food and hormones affect your body chemistry, and for ideas on how you can boost your energy levels.

Find your powerful purpose

Imagine how you would feel if you woke up every morning excited by what the day had in store for you. Imagine how positive you would feel if, when you imagine the future, it is a bright, compelling picture. Imagine how motivated you'd be if you were working towards a future you could be proud of, instead of dwelling on the mistakes, regrets and failures of the past. A life purpose is something you are passionate about doing or achieving for yourself or others. Passion is an energy source that can make you feel incredible. It's free, never-ending and has zero calories. In the hierarchy of human needs it's related to self-actualisation (fulfilling your potential) and is vital if you are to live a happy and meaningful life.

Human beings can be truly happy when all their basic needs are met and they are contributing to the life of other people. Your life's footprint is the sum total of the difference your life will make while you are alive on this earth. By considering what you would like that difference to look like, you can gather ideas for your powerful purpose. What are you passionate about? What would you want written about you on your tombstone? If you were guaranteed success, what would you spend the rest of your life doing? You might hear people referring to this as 'following your bliss'. There is a great theory that if you always enjoy what you're doing, you'll always be successful and happy.

Your powerful purpose doesn't have to be altruistic, though the more lives you touch, the better you will feel as you live out your dreams. Your powerful purpose might be to start an internet company and float it on the stock exchange. It might be to help end world poverty or to raise two healthy, happy children. Whatever the purpose is, why not throw everything you've got into making it happen? Give it your heart and soul and look forward to waking up every day of the rest of your life, excited about what's to come. It doesn't have to be sensible either. I set crazy goals for myself and it thrills me when they start to manifest. I never thought I'd be doing the things I'm doing in my life, but just by setting a goal, you begin to create it – so go for it! Have fun with it!

The secret of life

If you did nothing else, I would recommend having huge portions of fun and gigantic servings of laughter. See your positive friends as often as possible and vary the activities so that you're not always meeting up to eat or drink with them. Set some goals in your career or personal life, and discover what possibilities you can create just by believing in yourself.

STAGE 8 ACTION PLAN

Arriving at your weight-loss destination is cause for celebration and personal appreciation. It is also the beginning of a new cycle of life and a time of great change. The activities in this section acknowledge that positive change can be challenging as well as wonderful. You might need time to get to know the 'new' you. You might need to learn to say 'no' to previous habits and acquaintances. And you need a strong support network to keep you inspired, secure and feeling great. With your basic needs met and your mind in clear and positive focus, you are able to give time and energy to deciding on your greater purpose in life.

Your support network

- *List all the people in your life who support, love and/or encourage you.*
- *Be specific about how you would like them to support you (for example, listen, advise, look after the kids and so on).*
- *Brainstorm all the different and crazy ways you could add movement and variety to your life.*
- *Commit to doing one new thing a week with the help of your support network.*

Choose to say 'no'

Practise saying 'no' courteously and politely so that you can say it firmly and with confidence the next time you really don't want to do something you're asked. The hardest part will be telling the truth rather than making up an excuse. Just say 'no'.

Identify your powerful purpose

- *What are you passionate about?*
- *If you were guaranteed success, what would you do?*
- *What would you like written about you on your epitaph?*
- *What's your powerful purpose? What are you uniquely designed to do, given your life experience, upbringing and personality?*
- *Make a list of everyone you know and circle the names of those you could approach for help and advice to get you started on your powerful purpose.*

Fill in a copy of the questionnaire on pages 84–5 for every month from now until you reach your goal weight, then every two months after that. This is optional and only to be used as feedback on how well you're doing and as an indication of whether you need to improve something. Your focus should always be kept on where you are now and where you're headed, not where you've been.

APPENDIX

Affirmations

Affirmations are positive statements designed to be repeated until they program your subconscious mind to combat negative thinking. Over time this can make profound changes in your behaviours. Listen to each statement in a state of open, relaxed attention, breathing in with each one and repeating it to yourself out loud. Speak the following powerful daily affirmations out loud in front of the mirror, or recite them silently as you go to and from work.

Personal affirmations

I, ... believe with **every fibre** of my being, that I am a beacon of life, excitement and **pure positive energy**.

It is a **definite fact** that I have the **power** and **skill** to **create** and **manifest** anything I **desire**.

I **know** that my heart is filled with **love** and **peace** shining out like a lighthouse, touching the lives of everyone around me. I am a force for **good**!

I am a shining example of **health**, **wealth** and **happiness** for myself and everyone whose life I have the privilege of touching.

I **know** with absolute **certainty** that I have the **power** to change the world for the better. I am an **inspiration** to all.

I am loved and cherished by my friends and family. I honour this by **loving** and **nurturing** my own **mind**, **body** and **soul**. I am **slim**, fit and strong, eating clean, **life-giving** foods that make me **feel outstanding**!

Like a magnet as powerful as the sun, I **attract** towards me **everything I desire** in oceans of abundance.

I live with **great fullness**. I'm thankful for all that I have, for everything I have accomplished so far, and for all the wonderful things still to come.

All I have to do is **ask** and the universe will **send it to me**.

I **know** that when I **dream** it I will become it; when I **imagine** it, I will **create** it. I keep going until I get the **outcome I desire**. I will **never give up**.

I **believe** to my core that life is **exactly what you make it**, and ... **I dare to make it magnificent**!

Affirmations for weight loss

Every day I am becoming emotionally stronger.

I am prepared and happy to accept any uncomfortable emotions as they occur and allow them freedom to voice themselves and be resolved freely and easily.

I am learning more and more to release anger and resentments gently, learning that people do the best they can with the resources they have available, that I can live and lead only my life, not theirs.

Only the universe knows what is best for me, and I can respond to situations in a way that allows me to be happy and achieve my goals.

I can use surplus energy to release and resolve any repressed emotions.

I can change or avoid situations that would previously have caused me pain.

I can nurture a strong and healthy body and mind, lose weight and stay slim, paying attention to the messages I receive from my body and what they really mean.

I can use moments of quiet meditation each day to resolve problems and release emotions in a safe and calm way.

I can visualise the kind of body that I want to have and the kind of person I am becoming.

I can live the life I dream of and appreciate the wonderful feelings that right now has to offer me.

I can remember to breathe deeply, and relax. My heart sends blood to every cell of my body to provide oxygen, nutrients and love.

Exercise and movement can only help me feel wonderful, release endorphins and send waves of relaxation and calm through my muscles and my whole body.

I surrender all fear of movement. I am taking back control and know that my body is my friend.

I am in control of my body and I am giving my body the instruction to become perfectly healthy and slim.

I will embrace activity, allowing it to give me the rushes of endorphins and increased serotonin levels that my body's joyful movement is designed to provide.

I can bathe every cell of my body in positive emotions and love, allowing my body to look younger, lose excess weight and feel amazing.

New patterns of behaviour in my life will naturally form and continue day to day, helping me to feel the way I want and deserve to feel.

I become more aware that I am loved, and I honour those who love me, by nurturing my mind, body and soul.

I can fearlessly say no to things in my life that I will no longer put up with.

I can say yes more and more to the things I deserve in my life.

I am learning how extraordinary I am as I continue to fall in love with myself and my body.

My special qualities are revealed to me and begin to have a positive effect on the people in my life and draw them closer to me.

I am starting to feel excited about the control I am gaining over myself, my habits, my body and my life and where this journey is taking me.

I begin each day by focusing on my goals and what I want to achieve.

I am helping my body to look and feel better every day.

Peak performance coach Jessica Robbins

At the age of 19, and just a few days after winning the British Taekwondo Championships, Jessica's dream of becoming an Olympic contender was seemingly destroyed when she was diagnosed with a degenerative back disease. Instead, she went to University College, London, graduating with an MSci in maths and computer science, and went on to become an IT consultant in the City.

Several years later she 'woke up' to find herself stranded, far from the life she had dreamed of: six stone overweight, struggling with the constant pain of a back disease, in a job she hated and, unsurprisingly, depressed.

In 2004 she discovered NLP and hypnotherapy and used these powerful tools to transform herself in just six months. She took control of her life, gaining in confidence and self-esteem, and she lost the weight. She then became a performance coach so that she could help other people to achieve their dreams, and now coaches and inspires athletes, performing artists and business professionals around the world.

Jessica is driven by passion and curiosity to discover the limits of what is possible. One of her happiest moments to date was realising that she had cured her own illness and was finally free of pain. She sets many playful and exciting goals for herself, and has already achieved some of them, such as presenting her own TV show in March 2007. This book is also the fulfilment of a lifelong dream. Future goals include winning the Olympics and singing professionally.

Further information

For a wealth of further ideas and insights on how to lose weight without dieting please visit the website www.jessica robbins.co.uk. It is updated regularly with new affirmations and insights, and Jessica would be pleased to hear how you are managing to progress on your personal journey.

As an additional favour to yourself, download the hypnosis CD from the website and listen to it every day. Not only will it help you subconsciously to program your habits to work in line with your goals, but it will also allow you to spend some time every day enjoying good-quality relaxation, which will make you feel less stressed and better about life in general.

If you are interested in continuing your adventure of discovery, you are welcome to attend one of the 'Weight Loss without Dieting' live seminars held in London. Here you have Jessica's personal support, as well as the support and encouragement of others who want to help you succeed. You will also have the opportunity to do some of the exercises contained in this book, and some new ones just for fun, which will further assist you to make profound and astonishing changes in the way that you feel about yourself and your life, as well as the way you behave.

For additional information about this book, plus worked examples and podcasts, please visit:
htttp://www.pearsonbooks.com/loseweight

Acknowledgements

I am eternally grateful to my family and friends who have supported and encouraged me in my adventures these last few years. I could write at least another book on how wonderful each and every one of them is and the ways in which they have inspired and supported me, but I have only this little space, so to the following special people, I would like to say one big thank you for believing in me and filling up my life. I love you.

Elie Ball, Simon Hepworth, Alexandra Leonhardt, Pierre Hasanoui, Walid Farruque, Yon Badiola, Penny Hedger, Sophie Robinson, Jade Ashton, Fran Robinson, Ian Warner, James Burnett, Hannah Williams, Jane Mayfield, Patricia Lichfield, Simon Burnett, Steven Paul, Emma Robinson, Simon Duffil, Melanie and Des Robinson, Derek Bishop, Kirsti and Jamie Parslow-Williams, Jason Standing, Lucy and Steve Wilson, Daniel Jones, Adam Jay, Tim Minchin, Conrad Palmer, Raphael and Anja Socha, Marianne and Charlie at The Bluff, Tintagel, where this book was written, and Simon Edwards, who will always be my hero.

I would also like to give a huge amount of thanks to the wonderful people at Pearson who have given me so much support along the way – Emma Shackleton, Sarah Sutton, Patricia Burgess and Rachael Stock – who have the patience of saints.

Index